PARADISE

the Holy City
and the Glory of
the Throne

by Rev. Elwood Scott

D0943139

Engeltal Press
P.O. Box 447
Jasper, ARK 72641 U.S.A.
www.engeltalpress.com

Abridged Edition by Engeltal Press 1984
P.O. Box 447
Jasper, Ark. 72641
U.S.A.

Used by permission.

FOREWORD

"I go to prepare a place for you." (John 14:2)

The most positive words about the eternal abode of the saints are found in these words of our Saviour. He made heaven very real to us. Without Jesus, we would not know very much of what heaven really is like. He opened the door to the "land that is fairer than day" and let us have a peek into it. He was our greatest Authority because He had come from heaven and had complete understanding and knowledge of the celestial land.

In this last while many of us have suffered the loss of our dear loved ones. We have missed them deeply and often longed to see them again and share our earth-joys with them. When we realize they are no more with us here, in the physical form, it gives us much inward pain. In this last while the Lord has called many of His choice saints home to be with Him.

The only thing that can comfort our grief at the loss which we have suffered is the knowledge that they are with the Lord in the home which He has prepared for them. They are now waiting for us to come and join them there.

I personally believe that many more of His righteous ones will soon be called home. My own brother, Jamie, was called home very suddenly just a few months ago. The knowledge that He is with the Lord is my only comfort. When I bade my father good-bye at his death-bed it was a deep grief to me because I know He loved me very dearly. As he was passing from this world to the next, my mother, my husband Jim and I sang the songs of heaven to him. We sang while the angels dipped down low and carried him away into Abraham's bosom.

I was in Germany when my father was sick. I did not know if I would be able to see him before the Lord took him. I was having a terrible struggle in letting him go. One day the Lord made heaven so real to me that I was able to release my father. I began to write him a "good-bye" letter. Suddenly, the anointing came upon me and the prose turned into a poetic form of writing. I want to share this with you. If you have suffered the loss of a loved one, I pray that it will give you comfort.

You're standing at the gate of tomorrow,
And it's hard to let you go,
Even though it's a flesh good-bye.
Our spirits are united ever and you'll always be close by.

If you should leave this house of clay
Ere I return to bid farewell,
Then don't feel bad, my father dear,
You're going just ahead.

We are coming close behind
Mother, brothers, Jim and I
And we will meet again, dear dad,
Upon the other side.

You'll hug and kiss me with a smile
Like you have always done.
And I'll forget each lonely mile
My weary feet have run.

You know, I envy you a bit
Because you'll see HIM first,
The One who loved and lived and died
And took on Him our curse.

I've longed to see Him for so long,
I know I still must wait.
So tell Him that I love Him, dad,
When you step beside the gate.

And so, I bid you here good-bye,
"Auf Wiedersehen," dear dad.
Remember, your girl loves you still
And will really miss her dad!

Gwen R. Shaw

HEAVEN

I looked past the curtain of time,
And saw up the beautiful stairs
Ten thousand bright angels in glory
All dressed in white raiment so fair.
"The battle is over," I heard them,
Their voices rang out o'er the air.
With palm leaves they shouted "Hosanna,"
His glory forever we'll share.
Our troubles and toiling is over,
The tempter is under our feet.
He's cast down in darkness forever
While we walk the beautiful streets.
The flowers will bloom on forever,
The leaves of the trees evergreen.
No night will come to our city,
For it's lightened by heaven's bright beam.
As we stroll through the garden of heaven
And smell the lilies so sweet,
We'll clasp the hands of our loved ones,
As He says, "May your joy be complete."
As He shows us each one to our mansions
And we move in forever to stay,
The children will play by the fountain,
Our treasures will never decay.
We'll visit each other in heaven,
So often I'll knock on your door.
We can sit on the porch of your mansion
And look out o'er the beautiful shore.
We can talk of God's blessings for ages,
For time up there will never end.
We'll all have plenty in heaven,

I'll be just as rich as you then.
The ole ship of Zion is anchored,
They're stepping out onto the shore.
"The journey is ended," they shouted,
"We'll never sail seas any more."
The gates swing open so gently
As all of God's children pass through;
At last we hear Jesus say softly,
"I came here to fix this for you."

-Author Unknown

INTRODUCTION

For many months past I have had frequent visits from a very peculiar visitor. Although his visits have been surprises to me, yet they have been most welcome indeed.

At first I was startled and greatly surprised when a man with silken beard and flowing garments came into my study entirely uninvited and without apology.

At first his visits were brief, then longer. If I went for an evening's walk in the fields or woods, he would frequently drop into my company, and seemed delighted to walk with me. I soon found he could speak different languages with perfect ease and that his nationality was different from my own.

He seemed of superior ability and his intellectual powers were in ability far beyond my own. In short, he was a very uncommon person.

I have had a custom for many years past of rising early in the morning and taking a drive for an hour or two before breakfast. Not infrequently I have overtaken a man who asked me for a ride; but on a number of occasions after I had welcomed the journeyman to my side, I found, Philip-like, by the side of the man in the chariot — he was my silken bearded friend.

Frequently after an hour's conversation he would simply vanish from my presence without a moment's notice; and I have often looked in all directions, but in vain to see the course of his departure.

I have been entranced and lost in wonder and admiration at the trend of his conversation, and the nature of his revelations. My soul loved him exceedingly and was grieved at his departure. Sometimes, after the family had retired, he would steal into my room while busy at my studies and remain until after the midnight hour.

Among his earlier visits, one evening he asked me if I could still write shorthand.

"Indeed," I said, "with as much ease as in earlier days."

"I have been looking for you for some time," he replied, "and if you consent to serve the purpose for which I have sought you, I will confer a favored saint's blessing upon you."

I gave him all the assurance I could of obedience to any reasonable request he might ask. He then lovingly replied: "You shall then write a message for me to the people."

After the arrangements were all completed for its final disposition, he appointed an evening for a visit similar to those we had enjoyed so much when he took me by surprise. So from time to time we met and the results were the following pages which will explain this introduction.

I am glad I consented to write for him. It has been with continual wonder, surprise, and admiration, and has also been a great blessing to me personally.

During one of his earlier visits he explained that he was the same man I had met some years before on the mountain slopes of the Cascades. I remembered him quite well, for I had spent a day and a night in his cheerful home, and under his holy influence. His name was Seneca Sodi, a Greek of Jewish descent, a fine scholar, a firm believer in Christianity, and a thorough student of his Bible.

But he seemed so changed now, and his face glowed with such a halo of light that I did not recognize him at first and was inclined to doubt his story and to let it all pass as a clever trick, that I could not explain, that was being practiced upon me. Yet I could see a great similarity in the appearance of this man and my long bearded friend of the Cascades.

I said to him: "How can this be?" He quickly replied, in the twinkling of an eye, "Only an earlier sheaf in the great resurrection harvest."

"Oh, my God!" I said, "is it true that there is a man who has already experienced the great resurrection of the just, which is to occur at the last day?"

I thought then of the translation of Enoch, and of the chariot which swept Elijah into the heavens; of Moses, who twice fasted forty days and was alone with God upon the Mount of Vision until he had caught a radiance of the eternal glory.

I thought of Paul who had been caught up into the third heaven and heard words of the everlasting kingdom. I thought again of the many bodies of the saints which slept and arose after our Lord's resurrection; who went about Jerusalem showing themselves alive from the dead.

So I reasoned within myself, saying, may not great events occur in these last days of Gentile grace? Why should not Seneca Sodi, one of the descendants of the ancient Israel of God, in these last days receive great revelations from the Almighty and an earlier resurrection than the rest of the great harvest? But I must leave him to tell his own story.

Elwood Scott

CHAPTER ONE

Seneca Sodi's First Visit

It was the first day of June and the sun had set. The toil of the day was over. I had my studio thoroughly lighted and in the cleanest and best condition I could make it. I had provided pencils, paper, pens and ink, and was nervously waiting for my silken bearded friend. I felt a keen sense of uneasiness, not knowing the full nature of his mission or what all it might embrace. I knelt and most solemnly prayed that the Almighty Father might be my helper, for my visitor had impressed me with a sense of awe, and that I was quite insignificant in his presence.

The door at last opened and Seneca Sodi came in. A wonderful halo of light about his head and face.

I arose to greet him and with a pleasant "good evening" he apparently gripped my hand.

"My son," he said, "I greet you in the name of the Father."

When he had taken a seat, he said: "Do you remember my humble home at the foothills of the Cascades?"

"Indeed I do, and the long ramble among the hills we enjoyed together that day, and of the sleepless hours until after midnight and of my promise to endeavor to see you again in your little earthly mansion of bliss."

"I could not wait for your return," said Seneca. "Strange experiences were awaiting me. I had been earnestly hoping that the coming of the Lord was near at hand and was much in prayer. I was strangely impressed with the thought of coming great events, but was not expecting the great favors which were so soon to be shown to me. But I find that God takes delight in surprising us with new and great blessings.

The Story Begins

Dinner had just been eaten and I had lain down on the couch for a few moments' rest. My two servants, Sena and Serva, were busy about the house, when all of a sudden, a blast of a trumpet called us all to the door.

A beautiful chariot of gold and two drivers clothed in white garments were standing very near. Immediately I seemed to fall into a trance and was lost to earthly things for a time. The angels came into the room and urged me to prepare quickly, saying, "For the Lord of the kingdom has need of thee."

I could easily understand their errand and language. I was filled with exultant praise in the thought of immediately going home. Resuming consciousness of earthly things, I quickly arranged with Sena and Serva, who had only seen glimpses of glory in flashes of bright light, but felt the presence of invisible ones about the room, to guard carefully the body, should I leave it behind. I found myself in a semi-conscious state, and saw a number of holy beings about my bed, for I felt so weary, I had lain down. I had momentary thoughts flung across my mind: "Is this really death? Am I really going to say good-bye to worldly things this day? Am I truly in the borderland of eternity? If so, blessed victory!"

I felt, now creeping into my soul, the raptures of eternal joy — oh, such light and visions of glory which were granted to me then! Spiritual essences and things began to loom up before me with great vividness to my comprehension. I seemed to be passing out into a large place where a new order of things was existing. With one last effort to see and speak to my servants, I barely could say, "Good-bye," as I saw their anxious eyes looking into mine. I heard some broken sentences and tried to explain, when I thought they were far out of hearing, and I closed my eyes only to open them in an eternal day.

The next thing I observed was that I was standing in one corner of the room looking with deep interest upon my body, which was lying in quiet repose upon the bed. I cannot well describe the strange yet joyful feelings of my soul on finding myself released from the body. I came forward and stood beside the bed and with feelings mingled with joy and pity I said to my body, "I feel sorry to leave you behind, but you are still mortal and will be till the resurrection."

I next saw three angels with me who seemed busy with some peculiar embalming process for my body, which I did not understand. They spoke to me most pleasantly and said: "Be not afraid. We are come as your escorts to your heavenly home, the light of which shines so brightly upon you now."

How quickly I thought of that scripture: "The angels are all ministering spirits sent forth to minister for them who shall be heirs of salvation! (Hebrews 1:14) I soon came to realize that physical eyes cannot see spiritual beings nor comprehend their movements except by some miraculous intervention; but that spirits can comprehend both matter and spirit.

I found that my vision was greatly improved since being freed from the mortal body — nor did I regret now I was released, for everything seemed to shine with a luster and glow with a brightness I had never known before; and what seemed more remarkable still, was that the sunlight did not aid me in any sense to comprehend things about me, for I knew that at night when all the world were asleep and that it was entirely dark to outward human eyes, yet to me everything shone with a splendor more grand than the brightest noonday earth ever afforded.

Again and again the scripture came to me: "Yea the darkness hideth not from thee, but the night shineth as the day. The darkness and the light are both alike unto thee," (Psalm 139:12) and again, "there shall be no night there." (Revelation 21:25)

I saw distinctly a number of angels about the room, each of which was covered with robes of pure and heavenly light, so gladdening to my soul. I wondered why I could not have discerned them before, even while in the body. The scripture came to me where the prophet said, "The angel of the Lord encampeth round about them that fear him and delivereth them." (Psalm 34:7)

From this time I began to feel a strange upward bounding tendency. My spirit felt a mighty pull heavenward as though elastic cords were fastened to all parts of my soul, with the other end reaching into the skies.

Sena and Serva sat weeping by the bedside. I tried to speak to them, but could not arrest their attention. I walked near to them and laid my hand upon their heads, but still they did not comprehend me. They only seemed to weep more bitterly for there seemed to be a soul touch. Then again their tears would dry and they would scan the room as though some voice had been heard, and I felt sure they realized something of my presence without comprehending the truth as to how it was.

The angels now began to sing and oh such sweet music I never heard while in the body. When they had finished the anthem, they said, "Will you now follow us?" When we had

3

stepped outside, I saw the chariot which seemed to be made of light. It was standing still at the threshold. I understood its meaning and the special errand of the angels, and I longed to spring within, as I fairly shouted "Hallelujah," which I am sure the angels heard, for they quickly said, "Glory to God in the highest."

I tried to say good-bye to my sleeping body, the old home and my two servants when the angels hastened me to a seat with them in a chariot. They again assured me of a safe journey homeward. In a moment more the chariot began to rise with a swift and noiseless motion, and to me with an unknown speed, we were going on our flight toward the eternal mansions.

CHAPTER TWO

First Visit – Continued

No sooner had I taken my seat in the chariot than I found I could converse with the angels with perfect freedom. There seemed to be a kind of comprehension of ideas without the effort of words; and yet we spoke as spirits speak. I have often heard words spoken while in the body which were wholly in the ear of the soul, and yet most distinctly understood when there was no audible voice whatever – the same as at St. Paul's conversion: he heard a voice distinctly in his inner consciousness while those who journeyed with him saw no man from whom the voice came.

I now asked, "Are you really and truly angels of God, about whom we have read and sung and heard so much while in the world?"

"Truly we are," they replied, "but of our birth you know nothing, for in fact we were not born but created; not in the earth but in celestial regions. We have learned our lessons in the past eternities in the presence of God; but we are glad to be your servants and helpers now, and this has been our glad service ever since man was created upon the earth, but we can tell you more about ourselves at another time."

I replied, "We have been strangers until this time, but you make me feel great confidence in your ability to safely guide the chariot. I have been looking for this time for many years, but did not know it was so near."

"Oh," said the charioteer, "you need have no fears, I will conduct you safely to your eternal home."

"I looked out of the chariot again and saw we were passing with indescribable speed. The earth with its cities, towns and mountains were vanishing like a spector in the distance. We soon seemed to have the moon under feet as we mounted the pillars of the heavens. We had much conversation on the way. I found the angels most tender and lovely beings, so full of instruction and helpfulness; my soul loved them exceedingly. I felt as though I was acquainted with the heavenly kingdom, for the angels had told me so much. As I would look abroad from the chariot window, the stars could be seen everywhere just as I had always seen them from the earth; I knew then we had not

5

gone beyond the regions of the solar system, so I asked the angel: "Where is heaven?"

"Oh," said he, "it is not far away. The earth is the first habitation of man, and while he is of the earth he is earthly in his nature. Heaven is the future and everlasting habitation of all those who have prepared themselves for it. You will soon find that my words are true that heaven is not far away. Your Father's love and care have provided both these worlds for you. Your heavenly home is your real home. The earth was only your birthplace, the place of your beginning. But when God gave you eternal life He connected you with all heavenly realms, for He gave you His life which has always been. "Look and see," said he, for I was in the deepest consideration of these things for they meant so much to me now.

I looked abroad; we were just entering a region of bright clouds something like a glorious, glowing, earthly sunset, only far superior. The time had been very brief indeed, but we were actually slowing up in the great suburbs of the eternal kingdom.

"Listen a moment," I said to the angel, "what music do I hear? Is it real or am I in imagination?"

"It is the song of the redeemed in heaven you hear. All the heavenly kingdom is full of music without a discord."

No sweeter music ever fell on my ears. I was perfectly enraptured with delight.

"Are we near the gates of the city?"

"Very near to the portals of paradise," he said. At this the angels bowed their heads and covered their faces with their hands, while I fell flat on my face in the chariot. Stillness reigned in our souls, but deep emotions began to heave in my breast. I felt I must break the silence by shouting the praises of God. The angels now began to sing with a sweet voice, "Holy, holy, Lord God Almighty! Just and true are all thy ways, thou King of Saints."

I sprang to my feet and for a moment seemed perfectly bewildered with what met my gaze in every direction. The light was so transparent and far exceeding the most perfect day earth ever afforded. Clusters of heavenly flowers were growing everywhere. Groves of beautiful trees loaded with fruit, along with magnificent flowering shrubs beautiful beyond description met my eye in all directions. Roadways like winding streets arranged with exquisited taste and beauty, were penetrating this

6

pleasure ground of glory. Lovely souls were coming and going, passing and repassing each other with the salutations and courtesies that heaven only knows.

The chariot was now slowing its speed and such raptures of glory which filled my soul, I cannot describe them! I was simply lost in wonder, while I kept saying, "Surely I am at home at last." The chariot seemed trembling as a thing of life and finally halted beside a beautiful grove of fruit laden trees. The doors were opened and the angels stepped out. I fairly sprang with one leap to the solid foundations of the heavenly kingdom. For a moment I stood perfectly entranced as I saw so many happy souls clothed in white garments of lovely patterns, and all with such bright and happy faces beaming with perfect contentment and satisfaction.

I could contain my feelings no longer. I fell on my face again beside the angel, with loud thanksgiving to God; and was in the act of woshipping the angel for his great care of and kindness toward me, when he said, "Worship God only, I am also a fellowservant of his and this is my joyous service." At that he beckoned to one near by. He came and was introduced as one of the elders of heaven, who gave me such a cordial welcome that my soul loved him intensely at once.

The angel now said, "I leave you in his care, but may see you again shortly."

I put out my hand toward him saying, "I am sorry to see you go, you have been such a friend to me. What can I do for your great kindness to me?"

"Oh, you can soon help others," said the angel. So waving with his hand, and with a lovely smile, he said "Good-bye," and his chariot was gone.

The elder now said: "Well, my son, you are now at home. All that you see and infinitely more is the provision of your heavenly Father's love and almighty power. This is the borderland, my son, of the heavenly domain. Your sacrifices on earth were little when compared to your great gains here."

"Oh yes, and they were really nothing," I said. There comes to my memory a sweet passage of scripture which I never fully comprehend until now: "For our light affliction, which is but for a moment worketh out for us a far more exceeding and eternal weight of glory." (II Corinthians 4:17)

"Sure enough," said the elder. "You have only begun to

comprehend the glory; the weight of it you will yet feel."

"The grandeur and beauty of everything excels my highest expectation. Everything seems so real. Do tell me if I only fancy or am I in a dream, or is it really true that I am in heaven?"

"Oh," the elder replied, "it is a common thing for souls when they reach the heavenly world to seem bewildered when first ushered into the presence of angels and the spirits of just men made perfect, and the glory of this kingdom. It does, indeed, exceed the most sanguine expectation. No, my son, you are not in a vision, you are really here. Your body indeed is left behind you, and you will find that you have many things to learn ere you reach the throne in the Holy city. But be content, for I see you have thoroughly washed your robes and made them white ere you left your earthly habitation." "Be perfectly free," said the elder, "in asking any questions you may like; for the knowledge of this world is acquired by investigation and inquiry as was our earthly knowledge. Every desire you have will be fully met. All your cravings, desires and longings after the knowledge of your everlasting habitation have been fully provided for here. Your heavenly Father's will will be your will and all that you see, and infinitely more, are yours to enjoy forever. If you have made good use of your opportunities in your past life you have much treasure laid up in the city of which our Lord spoke while on earth and of which you will know more later on."

"I see," said the elder, "that yonder is another soul just brought from earth to paradise whom I must go and welcome." So saying, he went toward the chariot and there stepped out a lovely looking man, indeed, clothed in a robe of the purest white. The elder beckoned me to him. As I came near and heard this conversation I found he was from the opposite side of the earth from which I had come. He spoke a different language from my own and yet I understood him well. In a moment he lifted up his hands and clasping them together he said, "Oh, bless God forever," at which we both fell on our faces with adoring praise to our Almighty Father. We continued long for our souls were overcome with the raptures of this place.

When we arose, another saint, apparently of ancient times, came to him, and said, "Let me assist you in the ways of the kingdom." I heard him ask after his name. He answered: "I am Bohemond of northern Russia. Only a few hours ago I kissed my wife and children good-bye and embarked on a vessel on the White Sea at Oneida bound for the North Cape. I only remember that the vessel was sinking and we were many fathoms below the surface. Oh, do tell me, is this heaven or is it but the mariner's dream of home, when he is far away?"

"My son," said this venerable father, "You have safely landed, not at the North Cape nor in the bottom of the White Sea, but in your eternal home. Your body no doubt is in the depths of the briny deep; but the angel was with you as the vessel went down and has brought you safely here. Your body will be cared for in the resurrection day of rewards."

The elder who was with me said, "How rapidly we are gathering from all lands into our Father's house. This is only one of the many stations located in these distant portions of paradise. To these stations all souls come for their introduction into this heavenly home."

"How is that, will you explain to me?"

"Surely," he replied, "you will more fully understand as we go forward. You could not have endured the glory of the throne, without being prepared for it. Even now you could not endure the light so abundant within the city."

Just at this moment I saw a woman step from a chariot. She seemed to be so bewildered that she sank down as one of the attendants approached her. She threw up her hands and cried out in amazement, "Oh, my God! I am not worthy nor fit for this glory. Oh, can I ever be made right with God?" She closed her eyes almost unconscious with bewilderment and it seemed she could not speak as her attendant kindly addressed her with most loving words. At last she opened her eyes and looked about in wonder and amazement exclaiming, "Oh, these white garments, these golden goblets, trees of life and blooming flowers! I am not worthy of them. Have I really a right to be here and to all these beautiful trees loaded with such lovely fruit? Oh, the mercy of God! I was such a great sinner."

"Yes, indeed," replied her guide, "but your sins have all been forgiven. The angels make no mistakes. You have a right to these trees, for they are His on whom you have believed; yea they are yours, for you are His."

At this she arose to her feet and said: "But have I the

9

wedding garment on? I was earnestly trying when the chariot came for me. I was in such deep distress and confusion of soul, knowing I had not been prepared for so great a change."

"You have been saved, my child." said her attendant, "so as by fire, you were not a faithful servant of God, you did not build with gold, silver and precious stones, but with wood, hay and stubble, which have been burnt. God cannot reward you largely now. These infinite blessings spread out before you in all directions may be obtained by and by, when you are prepared for them. Be faithful to your present opportunities, for much is before you to be done. Advancements which ought to have been made in the world will have to be made here, ere you can go on to the city gates, or see the shining glory of the Jasper wall. Come with me and I will assist you in a further knowledge of Christ and His eternal salvation and kingdom."

I now said to the elder by my side, "Will you explain to me her great mistake?"

"Surely," he replied. "She represents a very large class in the world who have not made good use of earthly opportunities, she was never deeply interested in her salvation till near the time of her death. Do you not see how slim and lean she looks, and how little clothing she has, only a gown! Her repentance has been genuine and her faith accepted the promises of eternal life in her Lord, and her forgiveness has been complete. She has added but little grace and almost no growth to her soul. She feels now, as all such souls do and must feel, her great loss. She has no treasure laid up in heaven. Paradise itself seems too good for her; but God in His great mercy will bring her on. These trees are for her. Their leaves are full of healing virtue. No one who has not received the gift of eternal life and been born again will ever be carried by the angels to this glory. Many, alas, perish from the earth in sight of the Redeemer's outstretched arms of love and mercy, because they will not accept His gracious help; they love the pleasures of sin more than God or these everlasting joys and pleasures at His right hand here forevermore."

"Oh, blessed Christ," I cried, "filled with everlasting love and mercy for thy people, that even in the last moments of life, like the dying thief, may be snatched from the jaws of death! But, oh, her great loss, how sad!"

A group of happy souls now came toward us. The elder

10

introduced us. We were soon acquainted and conversed with each other with great freedom, although we had never met before. We seemed perfectly acquainted in a few moments and the visit was very pleasant indeed. One man fairly shouted the praises of God with loud hallelujahs, saying, "Oh, my God, I bless thee, I am in heaven at last!"

"Now," said Seneca, "I must leave you for the night. You are weary and tired and must sleep. I will see you again on the second evening from this," and he vanished from my room.
I sat musing. Where has he gone? Where does he stay? What is his food? Has he now no human association on earth? Can he not reveal himself to others as he has to me? When he comes again I must entertain him and find out, if possible, other secrets of his sojourn on earth.

CHAPTER THREE

Second Visit
Further Introduction Into Paradise

The day with its busy cares was passed. The evening was lovely indeed. The stars had just begun to show their presence in the twilight and I was waiting in my library at the appointed hour. The door opened and Seneca Sodi came in. I arose to greet him, and said, "Good evening," and tried to clasp his hand in mine, but felt no touch of a material palm to mine as is usual. He replied: "I am glad to see you, my son. Are you prepared?" I told him I was, but felt a strange feeling of awe mingled with fear. His spotless purity seemed to come before me, and my own sinfulness and unworthiness was so apparent; but I summoned all my courage and said, "I am ready for your message." He asked me, "Have you faithfully transcribed the previous message?" I told him I had and showed him the manuscript. He hastily looked it over with satisfaction and said, "You may now write," and he proceeded as follows:

It seemed most wonderful to me upon finding that I could converse with perfect ease and freedom with anyone I met, although we had been accustomed to different languages and tongues while on earth, and often had to speak through interpreters; but now I found, since I had laid aside the material for the spiritual, I could easily understand the thoughts of anyone. As rapidly as he could think I could read his thoughts. Matters of detailed explanation were not needed or required as I had been accustomed to while in the flesh, for if a subject was plain to any one with whom I was conversing, it seemed that at once it was just as clear to my own mind, so I was quite surprised to find how rapidly I could take in a knowledge of the spiritual realm, and yet a second surprise constantly met me: that of the great depth of divine truth.

For instance, many things I had learned from the Holy Scriptures, while in my flesh, were now opened with a depth of meaning I had never seen before. I could compare it to nothing better than to great layer after layer and strata upon strata of precious mineral rock, so that the deeper down and the further on one went, the more precious became the ore and the finer the metal. I said to the elder by my side, "How is this?" He quickly and smilingly replied, "God never gives the best He has to give; you will find later on, that truth is unfathomable." I now felt myself like a little fish just launching out from the mouth of a great river into a great and boundless ocean without a shore to be seen or depth that could be sounded.

My feelings were joyful beyond any power to describe to a mortal man of flesh and blood. It seemed that my entire spirit was in a perfect rapture of delight. I asked the elder, who seemed to take delight in remaining with me, how I was to account for this rapturous joy which was increasing so constantly in my soul, until I felt I would break out into shouting and hallelujahs. He said, "The spirit of God is the atomsphere of heaven; His joy becomes ours on a larger scale than what we ever knew while in our flesh. The great joy that you feel now is only a little foretaste of what you will feel when you are ushered into the city and about the throne."

Upon this I quickly remembered the Scripture where the prophet said: "In thy presence is fulness of joy; at thy right hand there are pleasures forevermore." (Psalm 16:11)

A feeling of praise was continually crowding up in my soul for utterance. I wanted to praise God, for ever giving me an existence, and still more for my salvation from sin, for changing my heart and bringing me into this glory. Nothing of an earthly character could have induced me to have gone back to the world. I seemed to laugh at the thoughts of the fear of death, which fear belongs only to the impenitent and the unsaved.

The elder, who seemed perfectly conscious of my desire, said to me, "You need not fear of giving utterance to your feelings, for everyone praises God here. Those praise Him loudest and most who have learned how to praise Him best while on earth."

The elder, whom I found to be Joshua of olden time, and who had been taking such an interest in my introduction into the heavenly state, now said, "Let us go to yon cluster of trees and sit down a moment. I noticed as we approached them that they were growing beside a great river whose waters were clear as crystal and sparkling with a light of which I had but a faint idea while I was in the flesh. The trees were beautiful beyond anything I had ever seen. Their form was so symmetrical and lovely, with no dead or withered branches. The leaves had such an aroma that the fragrance spread over everything and to all parts of the kingdom of God as I was told. Everyone was brought under its influence. I had felt the power of this fragrance long before I knew the source.

The elder now said to me, "Look across to the other side of the river;" where I saw clusters and groves of these trees lining the bank as far as the eye could reach. There I saw multitudes of redeemed souls clothed in the purest white and all of them seemed filled with the same spirit of praise which I had felt so constantly since entering the portals of the kingdom.

The elder again said to me, "Let us gather some of the fruit of these trees and then we will join that company yonder." I replied, "I would be quite glad to do so, for I have eaten nothing since leaving the body," and yet I felt no great sense of need. My hunger seemed more like what I had often realized while in the flesh when I felt a longing to hear a good gospel sermon. My guide now said, "What kind of fruit would you prefer? You can have your choice of things here just as you used to in the earth. If you feel faint or weary from your long abstinence from food, this kind (pointing to a certain pear-shaped and beautifully colored fruit) is what you need, for the tree has twelve kinds, as you see, upon it." I said with feelings of deepest praise, "Oh, how wonderfully God has provided for us! Twelve kinds of fruit on each tree, ripening their fruit every month, and the leaves never withering! Wonderful!"

"Here," said he, "pluck from the boughs on this side of the tree and eat." I did so, and much refreshing and enlightening grace as they imparted to me, it is beyond the comprehension of mortal man to know; it must be eaten to be understood. The taste of the fruit was delicious indeed. The earth never furnished anything like unto it for taste, not the orange, peach, nor melon. Nor would the fragrance of the rose compare with it. "When anyone eats of these trees," said the elder, "he can never die again, grow older nor feel weary; death hath no more dominion over him. One of these trees grew in the Garden of Eden. After our first parents had sinned against God, they thought to eat of the fruit of it also; but God said, "No," for had they eaten of it they would always have lived in that sinful, dying state. So a flaming angel was sent to guard it, and so man never eats of it until he has passed the boundaries of his earthly life."

14

"Now," said Joshua, "let us cross over." To my great astonishment I found we could walk upon the surface of the water, which seemed like a sea of glass, it was so transparent, and yet it was gliding and rolling along as beautifully as any stream I had ever seen on earth. I quickly remembered the Word of God by His prophet: "But there the glorious Lord will be unto us a place of broad rivers and streams; wherein shall go no galley with oars, neither shall gallant ship pass thereby." (Isaiah 33:21)

As we walked along, I asked him, "How is it that we do not sink in the water?" He said, "you seem to have forgotten that you have left your body behind you, and that you are now ready to be clothed upon with a far more excellent body than you have ever known. Your spirit cannot sink in these waters. You will soon find that you can go from place to place at will either in the air or upon the solid foundations of the celestial country; but let us hasten," he said, for I was inclined to linger at every fresh object I came in contact with, "for I must introduce you to that great company you see yonder."

As we went on, I glanced up and down the river and saw many other spirits, still later arrivals than I, passing on toward the gathering legions of the bloodwashed. Among them was my friend, Bohemond of Russia, whom I met as he stepped from the chariot only a short time before.

My soul was filled with such an inexpressible sense of praise to God for the unspeakable gift of eternal life and for such a rational sense that it was I, myself, who once had lived in a world of sorrow and death, the memory of which, with a conscious freedom from it, now filled my soul indeed with ecstasies of eternal joy.

"Now," said Seneca, "you are weary and need sleep. May God's good angel guard and give you rest." And so saying he vanished.

CHAPTER FOUR

Third Visit
Introduction to the Saints

On the second evening again I was waiting for him, not knowing certainly, however, that he would come at that time. But I hardly had my studio in shape for such a visitor until he was by my side. His garments shone with a peculiar brightness and his face was all aglow with the light of heaven. I said: "Seneca Sodi, do take a seat and explain to me the mystery of your body and your food. Both your hand and the fruit of your basket evaded the grasp of my hand."

"At another time, my son, I will make it clear to you. Are you ready for my message?" "I am," I replied. He then proceeded as follows:

By this time we had climbed the eastern bank and were approaching near to a multitude of happy spirits. Many of them turned toward me. The elder now said, "You will feel yourself entirely at home with them." And after a brief word of introduction, he said, with a pleasant smile, "Good-bye, I will see you again," and he was gone. Among the very first I met was the spirit of a dear man, an old friend of mine in Norway, and one whom I had known from his childhood. I had said farewell to him at a foreign port nearly four years ago and had not heard a word from him since, till I saw him among this multitude. We were soon face to face. He looked bewildered and in wonder. I said, "Truly, is this you, Mr. Hansen, the friend of my youth?" "Oh, indeed, and is this the face of Seneca Sodi?" and with that we clasped each other in our arms as redeemed souls only can. "I was not looking for you now, " I said to him, "you looked so well and strong when I saw you last." "Oh, yes, indeed, but I am here, and nothing could induce me to go back." He asked me, "How long since you came?" I was just proceeding to answer him when another stepped near to us whom I had known so well for many years. She was a noble Christian woman and a faithful servant of Christ in His vineyard on earth, who had turned many to the Lord. I had not heard of her departure from the earth, but here she was with such a halo of light about her head that at once I

16

thought of the words of the Lord: "They that be wise shall shine as the brightness of the firmament; and they that turn many to righteousness as the stars for ever and ever." (Daniel 12:3)

I saw also among the great company the spirit of an infant which had so lately passed away. The one having it in charge said its mother had wept and grieved much and many had tried to comfort her on the day of its death, but that her sorrow was too great to receive much consolation. "Oh!" I thought, "if she could only see it now in this glory and with such care she would quickly brush away her tears and rejoice in the way God has provided for all His children." I at once began to think of many of my friends and dear relatives who had gone on many years before. "Where are they now?" I wondered. So I asked one of the earlier arrivals if he knew the system or order here, in reference to those who had left the world years ago. "Oh," said he, "they have gone on to the city itself, of which you see the light yonder in the distance," pointing toward the source of the river. "Shall we not go there soon ourselves?" I asked. "Yes," said he, "as soon as our company is made up, which is now nearly full."

I looked across the river from whence I had just come, and saw quite a number gathering about the trees and could hear them most distinctly shouting, "Bless the Lord, oh my soul!" I saw others gathering from various points all of whom seemed to have escorts or ministering spirits to guide them in their first introduction into the heavenly country. I thought again of that precious word of God. Carried by angels into Abraham's bosom. Abraham's joy is certainly come now, I whispered to myself. Then I modestly and reluctantly asked, "Is Abraham anywhere about here?" and referred to that Scripture just quoted. "Oh!" they said, "he was just here just a little while before you came, but was suddenly called into the city on some important errand, for everyone here is engaged in a joyous service for our Lord. No doubt he will be here again soon as he or someone of the elders or ancients always guides these gathering hosts to the gates of the city."

I seemed now to be conscious that we were somewhere near one of the great entrances or gateways into the heavenly world, where all the souls from certain sections of the earth are brought and welcomed. From the very moment of my de-

17

parture from the body there was a constant and mighty drawing of my soul upward toward the throne of God. It seemed scarcely possible for me to remain upon the earth even to take one last look at terrestrial things, for I knew I had passed beyond the limits of time into a boundless eternity. I wondered deeply why I felt that strange feeling and tendency to bound upward, and so I felt a freedom to ask one near me if he could give me an explanation. "Oh!" said he, "we all felt just the same. It is the law of spiritual gravitation which draws all beings, which have been purified and made holy, to this great kingdom where God is. No doubt you have often felt something of it while yet in the flesh. Sometimes you inwardly sighed and longed to be freed from your mortal flesh. The drawings of this gravitation were such that during sickness or sore trouble you have often said, "Oh! that I had the wings of a dove, then would I fly away and be at rest." It was that which made St. Paul say as you will no doubt remember, "It were better for me to depart and be with Christ." (Philippians 1:23)

"Ah, yes," I replied, "I see that now; but it is not the case, I am sure, with all souls when they leave the body without any regard to their moral or spiritual state."

"Oh, no," said my friend, "there are two great centers in the spiritual universe of God. They might be compared to the two poles of a magnet with which no doubt you were acquainted while in your probationary state, the positive and the negative. All souls are drawn toward one of these two places, according to their respective condition. God's throne is the great center of his everlasting kingdom of light; toward it, all gracious spirits, who are blood-washed, are drawn from the time they accept Christ and were born of him, with more or less conscious power according as they yielded themselves to His holy will, and were transformed into His blessed image."

"I understand fully what you mean," I replied. "I knew something of it while in my earthly life and have often spoken of it to those around me; but will you tell me, in a word, more about those who chose a sinful life in the world?"

"Just the opposite," he replied, "they are drawn with a mighty force downward toward the pit of eternal death, where death shall always reign."

Just at this moment I saw one coming toward me whom I recognized as my old grandfather, who had been gone from the

18

earth for more than thirty years. He was a very faithful servant of God during his lifetime on earth. He was old and gray when he left us; but here he was in the beauty and vigor of manhood. "Oh, Seneca!" he said, "you are home at last."

"Indeed," I said, as I clasped him in my arms, embracing each other with a love-kiss earth never knew. His words of welcome were so heavenly. We both shouted out: "Bless the Lord, oh, my soul!" He asked many questions about relatives and friends; the condition of the church where he used to worship; how long since I left the earth, etc.; but I soon found that his questions were more like the queries of one of the elders of heaven when he asked the beloved disciple in Patmos: "What are these that are arrayed in white robes? and whence came they?" (Revelation 7:13) The elder knew better than John himself. I soon discovered his superior knowledge even of terrestrial things which had transpired long since his day on the earth. I remembered then, oh how forcibly! that in the blessed book it says that the angel which talked with John while in Patmos said, "I am thy fellowservant, and of thy brethren the prophets, and of them which keep the sayings of this book." (Revelation 22:9) I said to him: "How is it you know so much about the things of the world since you left it?" "Oh!" said he, "we have great liberty here in the vast domain of this great kingdom of Almighty God. Many have come since I entered the portals of heaven whom you know well. We have had many long and precious visits. They have told me much." "I trust that in due time we can have such a visit," I replied, "for I am so glad to have met you." "Indeed we will," said grandfather, "but yonder comes Abraham and I want you to meet him." "Sure, I shall be gladdened beyond my power to tell you for I have read and heard of him all my life. Oh, my soul! so many wonderful favors are shown me."

CHAPTER FIVE

Third Visit — Continued
Seneca's Further Visit with the Saints — Abraham and Others

"Are you sure it was Abraham you saw?" I asked my grandfather. "Oh, indeed! I know him well." "Then," I replied, "I shall be quite glad to see him, for as you know, his name was a household word among us on earth. Will you please tell me which he is, for there are so many saints in shining garments coming and going. I was asking about him just before I met you. I used to wonder very much what kind of looking man he was, and have often thought I would be delighted to see him. I have greatly admired his faith that never staggered, and his obedience to go where his eye could not see. How precious to us were the words concerning him. "Abraham believed God and it was counted unto him for righteousness." (Romans 4:3)

"I do not see him at present," said grandfather, "but he was among that group yonder that is coming along the bank of the river. He has turned his course from us just for a little while, for I see he has gone to welcome a company of new arrivals, who have just crossed the river. I see by his movements he intends to conduct this company to the city, where they will be introduced to the Lord Himself."

"But grandfather, if we go on to the city presently will I see you again? "

"Oh, yes," said he, "I shall be there quite often and we shall have much opportunity of talking on all past events, as well as what is before you. I have many things I wish to say to you. After you have been recognized by our Lord Jesus and confessed before His Father and the angels, you will then have abundant liberty to go as you will. I have just come from the throne itself and have left many that you will recognize when you are there. Your dear mother, who has been gone from you for more than fifty years is aware that you have entered the portals of the heavenly kingdom. She would have come with me at this time for she is very anxious to see you; but she was detained on some very important matters for her Lord. No doubt she will meet you ere you arrive at the city gate; but just now I must hasten on for there is an old friend with whom I was a playmate in earth, who has just arrived. We were bound together like David and Jonathan. When I left the earthly shores, he took it very hard, and now for many years he has been very lonely. He has just been carried by the angels into this our glory and I am going now to give him my welcome and bring him to this great company. There is an unusual stir about the throne today which Abraham can explain when you meet him. He will introduce himself when he comes. I hope to return in time to go with you up to the city," and waving his hand he said good-bye.

I watched my old grandfather as we used to call him in the earth. He walked off so gracefully or rather bounding like a young man. He used to be old and decrepit; but now his youth is renewed like the eagles' and every expression of his face was joy.

At this moment I turned around and to my great joy a most lovely person was coming very near me. He bore marks of great age, and yet for all that, he had an indescribable youthful appearance. He was not like the other spirits that I was accustomed to seeing. The elder that I first met and he were very much alike.

"Is this Abraham?" I said.

"It is," he replied.

"In the bosom of Abraham!" (Luke 16:22) I said softly, and began to bow myself down before him, for a certain feeling of awe filled my soul.

"Stand up, my son," he said, "we are all brethren here." Then he clasped my hand in his and with his other drew me close to him and gave me his kiss of welcome. Oh, such a freshness of love and joy which burst upon my soul, so that I fairly shouted, "Hallelujah," and said again, "In the bosom of Abraham!"

"Dost thou remember that Scripture?" he said. "Well, thou wilt realize its meaning more and more; but who is this by thy side?"

"Bohemond," I replied, "who also has just come from the world."

He then gave him his cordial welcome and said, "The great joy and gladness which you now feel has been mine during a hundred generations of earthly lives. Some day I trust I can introduce you to Lazarus, of whom it was said by our Lord, 'He was carried by angels into Abraham's bosom.' " "I see,"

21

said he, "you have just arrived and have much wonder and many questions to ask about this heavenly kingdom of our Lord. While we talk for a few moments let us be refreshed with a drink from this crystal river, for it flows from the great palace up at the throne. Would you like to taste its waters?"

"Oh, indeed we would, I have sung hymns, and read in the Holy Scriptures concerning this very river, where the angel pointed it out to John, who in his vision saw it proceeding out of the throne of God and the lamb." (Revelation 22:1)

He now proceeded to the brink and with a golden goblet he dipped and filled the cup for me, and another for Bohemond, and said: "My sons, drink of this river and you shall never thirst again, nor be faint, nor weary for its lack, for its waters shall never fail."

As I drank from the cup I said, "Oh praise God for such a supply! So sweet to the taste! How full of invigorating power! It makes me feel the joy and glow of youth."

"You never can feel old or weary again, after drinking of this living water," said Abraham, "for it is the water of life. I just now gave a drink to a company of fresh arrivals before coming to you. Did you not hear them praising God? They, with that great group near them, are now learning to sing together, in which you will join them, the song which we will all sing at the city gate shortly. Some of them have it quite well now and others knew it when they came, for it is contained in the Holy Scriptures on earth. God has revealed the order so that all might be familiar with it. Do you remember the song?"

"Please repeat it for me," I said, "that I may know which song you mean."

He replied: "John was caught up in spirit so he heard the strains of this music and wrote: 'I heard a great voice of much people in heaven, saying, Alleluia, salvation, and glory, and honor, and power unto the Lord our God: And God from the throne said, Praise our God all ye His servants, and ye that fear Him, both small and great. And I heard as it were the voice of a great multitude, and as the voice of many waters, and as the voice of mighty thunderings, saying Alleluia: Let us be glad and rejoice and give honour to Him: for the marriage of the Lamb is come, and His wife hath made herself ready.' " (Revelation 19:1,5,6,7)

"Oh, yes," I replied, "I remember that song so well and can join with them singing it now." I said, "Father Abraham, shall we not soon go on to the throne? I have such a desire to see my Lord Jesus, I have loved Him these years, and then I have many loved ones beside that I feel sure are about the throne."

"Your desires, my son," he replied, "shall be fully met. The patience you have learned on earth is of great service to you here. So I hope you will feel that restful, quiet trust in all God's ways."

"Oh yes, my whole soul says, 'Thy will be done.' "

"You will soon see the King in His beauty, and probably some of those who knew you best, may come out and meet us on the journey toward the city gates, for they certainly know you are here. Just as soon as our company is full we will be off. Twelve legions make the company, and you see they are gathering from all directions.

"Cast your eyes down the stream and you can see another company rapidly filling up. Look across to the other side and farther up the stream and you see another. The guides who welcome them soon know to what company and place each belongs. Some have made but little preparation for this glory ere they left the world, and now the light is too great for them; and, as you see, they fall back into the rear and content themselves among the trees, waiting for a further preparation by an application of these wonderful leaves of the trees. But all these companies you see will soon be gathering about the gates of the city."

CHAPTER SIX

Third Visit — Continued
Preparations for the City

"Father Abraham, may we ask you a question while we are waiting for these gathering hosts that make this company?"

"Certainly," he replied, "use your greatest freedom."

"I have just met my old grandfather, who has been here for more than thirty years. I had a long talk with him before you came. He has told me many things concerning this eternal world of light; but just as he was leaving me, to welcome another friend of his, he said there was considerable commotion about the throne just now. Would you care to explain it to us?"

"Oh, most gladly. Great events are about to occur of the most interesting character that time and eternity has ever known. Our Lord has recently announced that the time has nearly arrived when He shall leave the mediatorial throne and in company with all the saints and angels, will descend to the earth for its judgment, for the cup of its iniquity is now nearly full."

"Oh," I replied, "we have been expecting Christ's coming to the earth for many years. Some had even gone so far as to have dates set when He would return."

"But," said Abraham, "that was their folly. Our Lord had distinctly told them as you will remember in His word, and we have faithful copies of the Holy Scriptures here in heaven to which we have access whenever we choose, that no man knoweth the day nor the hour; even the angels themselves did not know nor even now do they know. (Mark 13:32) None of us who have been here during great cycles of eternity have known when the time would be and even now the exact period has not been announced. But notable events are announced at the throne during the great convocation, when millions of saints and angels are met for the great praise services of which you will know more later. All of us here, like those upon earth, are deeply interested in this great event, which the Father hath kept in the secrets of His own counsels."

"The church on earth and in heaven will soon unite in one great jubilee and celebrate the final and great victories of the cross of our Lord, at the resurrection of all the saints, from the days of Abel to the end of the age. The living saints of earth

24

as you know will all be changed in a moment, in the twinkling of an eye, and with divine permission and arrangement, we in heaven will all go back to the cradle of our nativity and say good morning to the church on earth. Then the great resurrection shall occur. Then will follow the earth's great sabbath. Although we have been here for long ages, yet we have looked with great interest towards this event. Tender memories cluster about the scenes of childhood and early youth, and we feel glad to know we shall soon visit the place of our early experience in the world and the scenes that witnessed our salvation from sin. And then we shall receive the fullness and completion of our salvation. The redemption of our bodies. A very few of us have already had our resurrection as you see in my own case."

"I have been waiting for some time to ask," I replied, "what made the great difference between your appearance and those other happy spirits and even my own?"

"All the elders," said he, "received their resurrection at the time our Lord was raised and with Him became the first fruits of those who slept; yet we ourselves shall be freshly arrayed along with you for the marriage of the Lamb, a great event to which we all are looking."

"Oh," I said, "Blessed be the Lord our God! My soul is in perfect rapture for His unspeakable gift."

"You may well be," said Abraham, "and it will never die away from your soul. The time is almost here and the angels and saints have carried the tidings to the utmost bounds of this heavenly domain. The Holy Spirit also, who is the light of the church on earth, as well as in heaven, is impressing the minds of the most godly in the church militant with this great event. I will speak to you again of this if you desire; but I see our company is now about full and we must prepare to be off for the holy city."

"The conduct, you will find, of all this great throng will not be the same, although nearly all are fresh arrivals from the earth, and with but little exception, all are anxious to see the King in His beauty. Some were exceedingly joyous; and others not so much so. Some have not made good use of their opportunities while on earth, and have not filled their souls with good. They have not been given to much prayer and efforts to develop the fruits of the spirit with themselves, which makes up the character for eternity. They have been building with wood,

25

hay and stubble, instead of gold, silver and precious stones. But feel yourselves entirely at ease, for we shall soon be off for the city."

Again he passed us, and stopping, said: "I see your observations. You have been noticing some who, as we have been preparing for our journey to the city and the throne, are inclined to drop into the rear, and are not so much filled with rejoicing." "Yes," I said, "and I think I understand it. I remember while on earth, many of God's children never could be prevailed upon to enter heartily into the way of life; their faith was weak and unsatisfactory; and in times of great rejoicings in God, they had but little relish for the deeper things of the kingdom. They lacked what we called real true consecration to God. Sometimes, we almost questioned whether they were saved from past sins. · It was a rule among us that those who had a clear knowledge of much forgiveness always loved much, and those who were filled with the blessed Holy Spirit, had a sense of great victory over the world, the flesh and the devil, and were of those who overcame and had right to the tree of life and to enter in through the gates into the city. These were filled with great rejoicings of soul, and it seems that the same disposition is extended into the heavenly kingdom."

"Thou art quite right, my son," said Abraham, "and when those, lean in soul, arrive here, they have but little relish for the crystal river, nor could they enjoy the fountains at the throne, nor do they have great relish for the fruit upon the trees of which no doubt you have been eating. They take more largely upon their coming here, of the leaves, the fragrance of which is so sweet and powerful upon you."

All the time he was speaking to me there was constantly coming to my mind the words of the apostle: "Every man's work shall be made manifest, for the day shall declare it; because it shall be revealed by fire, and the fire shall try every man's work of what sort it is. If any man's work shall abide which he hath built there upon, he shall receive a reward. If any man's work shall be burned, he shall suffer loss, but he himself shall be saved, yet so as by fire." (I Corinthians 3:13-15)

"Oh," I said, "how blessed that they have the foundation itself, the atonement made by our Lord Jesus Christ and the privilege of these leaves which I remember are for the healing of the nations." (Revelation 22:2)

Abraham then said to me: "God cannot reward them largely, for their lack of capacity to receive, and yet as full as they are prepared to do so they will enjoy the glories of this heavenly kingdom. One star differeth from another star in glory. They that be wise shall shine as the brightness of the firmament and they that turn many to righteousness shall turn many to righteousness as the stars forever and ever." (Daniel 12:3)

"Now," said Seneca, "I must let you rest, you have faithfully served me, and are weary. I will see you again on the second evening," and he bade me good night and was gone.

CHAPTER SEVEN

Fourth Visit
Enroute for the City

At the appointed hour my silken bearded friend came in and with the usual greeting, I welcomed him into my studio, and said:

"Seneca Sodi, I am most deeply interested in your narrative, and was anxiously waiting your coming."

"Are you ready?" he asked. I told him I was. He then proceeded as follows:

By this time everything was ready and we were off. Twelve legions of souls from various places had gathered in a very short time beside the river and all had come by the way of the cross. It did not matter what language we had known on earth, we could fully understand each other there, and all were speaking, as we passed along, of the precious salvation through Jesus. As I turned myself from the themes of my former conversation and began to mingle more freely with the group of joyous spirits, I met some whom I recognized as old friends. One dear lady whom I had known as an invalid for many years, and yet a very spiritual Christian, was in the group. She was rejoicing with exceeding joy. I cannot tell how we recognized each other, but there is such a similarity of the spirit itself to the bodily features that we at once knew each other, and memory was so fresh that we seemed never to have forgotten anyone. She seemed so well now, and her face was beaming with immortal youth. As I drew near to her there was a halo of light and heavenly joy, beyond my power to describe to you, covering all her soul. As I spoke to her, calling her by name, she at once seized my hand, exclaiming "Glory be to the Father. Saved, saved, forever! All sickness and suffering over! Hallelujah!

"Yes," I said, "and how well you look. Old things are passed away."

"Indeed, when you knew me I was a great sufferer. I realize now Paul's words, "For our light affliction which is but for a moment worketh for us a far more exceeding and eternal weight of glory." (II Corinthians 4:17) My soul is so full of glory. We are getting so near the King in His beauty. Oh,

28

listen! What do I see and hear? Oh, the chariots of God are coming!"

At this we fairly shouted, and could hear very lovely music in the distance, and looking in the direction from whence it came, we saw a great retinue of angels with flaming chariots of light coming toward us. I cried out, together with many other voices, as we caught the first glimpse of them."

"Oh, Father Abraham, is this our Lord Jesus for whom we have been anxiously looking so long?"

Abraham lovingly replied: "These are the chariots of God under the conduct of angels. They will soon be among you, bringing many ancient loved ones to greet you with a welcome ere they carry you to the city and the throne itself. You remember how it was on earth, when our friends came from long journeys, how we would go long distances to meet them. I used to go far down from Hebron to welcome Lot and his children. Isaac went a long way into the fields when he knew the camels and Rebecca were coming. In your day you went to the railroad stations and the wharfs of the shores to meet your loved ones. They keep up this custom in heaven."

In a few moments more — swifter by far than the fastest express trains of earth — they came nearer and nearer, and with a great sweeping circle they seemed to pass us by; but at Abraham's suggestion the great legions now parted, standing in two long groups with an open space or aisle between, to give the chariots room to pass. Soon, they began to slacken their speed and moving slowly but most graciously they passed between the long rows of spell-bound, anxious souls. We all stood as in breathless silence not only spell-bound but in amazement and great wonder, at the marvelous sight. The chariots and all within glowed with a brightness and glory which we knew were reflected from the throne itself. So when they had finally halted, they gave one great shout of hallelujah to God, saying His redeemed are here.

No sooner were the chariots standing among us than we saw they were filled with happy, shining ones. They soon sprang out and were among us. They had come to meet and welcome us to these realms of everlasting light and day. But who were they but acquaintances, friends and relatives whom we had known so well on earth, and who knew of our coming. We used to have reunions on earth, but they could in no wise compare to the joy of this meeting. Some of these had been there for many years. In a few moments more, many were embraced in each other's arms. Oh, such joy I never knew before, and such welcome! "Oh, blessed rewards!" I cried.

Among these was my own dear mother. She had died many years ago. How she knew me I cannot tell, nor how I knew her I do not know; but she rushed toward me and I knew her so well and said, "Oh, mother, is this you?" She was beautiful and lovely. She embraced me in her arms and said, "I knew you were coming." The memories of childhood and all her wonted smiles and kindness which a mother's love suggests, came back to me. There were many others like myself. Mothers and sons, fathers and children, old friends meeting again. The glory and joy of the occasion excelled anything I had yet known. The charioteers now kindly invited us all to take passage with them. We accepted, of course, with thankfulness, their offers of kindness and were soon within the chariots and the whole multitude were praising God. In a few moments we were flying with great speed toward the city gate, following the course of the river.

"The light toward the city which I had seen on my first arrival, grew more and more glorious as we neared the city. We could at length see the shining of the jasper walls. Although we were rolling along at such great rapidity the wheels were noiseless and the chariots without a jar. The appearance of the landscape on either side seemed at a distance like a sea of glass mingled with fire; but on a closer examination it seemed that it was immortal. Flowers of unfading glory, and with an endless variety of colors, many of which I never saw anything before to which I could compare them and their indescribable loveliness attracted universal attention. We saw thousands of angels and happy spirits passing in all directions; but all I saw seemed very joyous and happy in their work. I thought of the word of the Lord: "He maketh his angels spirits and His ministers a flaming fire."

I said to my mother: "Can you tell me why we were not brought directly to the throne at once when we departed from our earthly home?" "Oh," said she, "you could not have endured this glory, but would have been dazzled into utter confusion and unconsciousness. Even now your expanding powers cannot take in all the glory and grandeur of the city until you are further prepared for it. The same law prevails in heaven as on earth. The Patriarchal and Jewish systems were very inferior to the Christian dispensation and the kingdom of heaven on earth was very inferior to the kingdom here, as you see, in point of glory and blessing. So you could not be ushered in about the throne till you were graciously prepared for it. But I am so glad you are here. I had word of your coming ere you reached the portals of paradise, and I have often had word concerning you since I left you. This very angel which you do not recognize, who is your charioteer, has often been to you. Once when you were very ill and away from your home and came well nigh dying, he was by your bed all the night and laid his hand upon you and said you should live and finish your work. He has told me how he saved you on the water once when you came near being drowned."

"Oh, mother, was he there at that time?"

"Indeed, my son, and his own hand righted your little boat when it was almost overturned."

"Well, mother, I always felt there was some mysterious Providence which saved us that day; but how little I knew this angel of heaven was with me then. Oh, thank God for His wonderful care!"

"Yes," said mother, "at one time, he told me, he kept you from getting on a railroad train, which if you had, your life would have been lost, and your work not been done. Do you not remember many times when strange Providence came into your pathway and you wondered and sometimes grieved at their occurence? He was guarding your life and shielding you from the stormy blasts of danger. Some day you can ask him all about these times, and we ourselves will talk it all over, for we are just in the springtime of our eternal life. But do you see we are nearing the golden gate, glistening with one great pearl, studdened with a thousand shining gems? In just a little while we will all join in singing the Song of Moses and the Lamb? Do you know it?"

"Yes," I replied, "for we have been singing it far back in paradise where this great legion was made up." I repeated it over in a subdued tone to my mother, but wanted to shout it out at the top of my voice.

"Here," said she, "take this harp I have brought for you." She loosened it from a golden girdle about her and gave it to me. "See, I have one like it."

CHAPTER EIGHT

Fifth Visit
Just Outside the City Walls

Seneca came as usual and proceeded with his narrative, as follows:

Just as we were coming near the great gateway one of the elders came and met us, saying: "All welcome, ye children of God. Your Redeemer stands just inside the gate yonder at which you will soon enter." The elder made such a lovely bow and his words were so cordial and full of love it seemed to send a thrill of gladness over every soul.

I cast my eyes up at the majestic wall. It was of great height and shone with a brightness I cannot describe. It rested on twelve massive foundations, each having the name of one of the apostles above it, and so they decreased to the twelfth and presented the appearance of a majestic stairway. The name of Peter was written on the first foundation. Paul on the second, John on the third, James on the fourth, and so on to the top. From this topmost foundation, garnished with an amethyst, the wall rose to a great height. The light streaming from these foundations was most precious. Just here I noticed Abraham passing near by, and I asked him the mystery of the wall and its foundations.

"Oh," said he, "this wall is the eternal security of God's people. As long as this wall shall stand they are eternally safe. The mighty truths of God, promulgated by the apostles, as taught by our Lord Himself, is our eternal safety. Certain of the angels many long years before my time on earth, abode not in the truth, and God cast them out and they fell into eternal darkness and shame. But now this wall, of which you can see but a very little portion, entirely encircles this great city, and within the truths suggested by these foundations we shall ever abide, going in and out and finding everlasting comfort. You see that great Judean gate yonder? Its frame and hinges are of the purest gold and set with one great pearl. This gate always stands open for there is no restraint in heaven. Unbounded liberty is now yours forever. And the wall has respect to these without as well as to those within. The angel at the gateway is

32

to give direction to all who may inquire. You will further remember that there are twelve of these gates as well as twelve foundations and there are twelve angels as well as twelve gates. No man can enter these gates not fully prepared. Did you notice some who dropped back far into the rear? In the world the truth had to be observed for any advancement. This wall with its gates marks a definite experience in the career of the redeemed. It is a fuller development of the great truths suggested by the ancient tabernacle, the holy and the most holy place; has reference to the saints on earth and in heaven.

Just at this time I noticed many happy souls with the glory of God upon them, coming through the gateway toward us. They were all clothed in the purest white and each with a harp in his hand. As they drew near us, there began to be a general recognition of each other. These had been redeemed from the sections of the earth from which we had come. Many of them were old friends who had passed from the earth many years ago, yet whom we had known so well in early life and, as soldiers in the Lord's army many of us had fought His battles together.

The recognition was so full and memories so fresh it seemed as only yesterday when we had parted from them, when they said good-bye and sailed toward the harbor. There was no attempt to restrain feelings for they could not be restrained. It was one hallelujah to God. They seemed as much delighted as we. I thought again how faintly we had believed God's word in the earth and yet how divinely true it was. We spent a long time in shaking hands and in love's embrace, with a conscious sense that we were now united in an eternal union. I thought again of Paul's words: "Now we see through a glass darkly, but then face to face." (I Corinthians 13:12) Many angels were mingling among us and seemed in great delight at witnessing our joy. One of them said to me: "We have been watching over you since your infancy in the world, looking forward to this very time. We rejoice with you and have an increasing joy as we behold your own."

Abraham now stood up prominently before us all and with his hand beckoned for silence, and said: "I wish now to repeat to you all a portion of God's Word which I know you will recognize: "But ye are now come unto Mount Zion and unto the city of the living God, the heavenly Jerusalem, and to an innumerable company of angels, to the general assembly and

33

church of the first born which are written in heaven; and to God the Judge of all, and to the spirits of just men made perfect and to Jesus the Mediator of the new covenant, and to the blood of sprinkling which speaketh better things than the blood of Abel." (Hebrews 12:22-24)

Indeed it brought it fresh to all our memories; for our hearts were burning with great emotion; but scarcely did we know what to say, we were so over-awed at our surroundings, and the real consciousness that it was ourselves and our friends who had met in an undying state and in a sinless country, and in the presence of some who had lived thousands of years ago amid customs so different from our own, also face to face with the angels of whose birth we knew nothing, among all whom I saw none seemed aged or feeble. Some that I had known in the earth as old men now seemed young and the very picture of health and enjoyment. The angels also were clothed with youthful appearance and vigor. I said to one of them: "How is it that lapse of years does not make its mark upon you here?" "Oh," said the angel, "one day here is as a thousand years of an earthly existence. No one ever grows older in appearance or feelings in this world. We are undying and undecaying. We are clothed only with immortality. No one ever feels a pain or knows a sorrow here."

Just at that moment, a woman who had been standing near and listening to the conversation, clapped her hands with ecstatic joy and said: "Oh, blessed be God for such a deliverance! I was greatly afflicted for thirty years before I was released from my earthly pain and sorrow. I was reduced to poverty and want, often spending many days and nights alone and lonely. My sickness was of long duration and my suffering was great. Occasionally a passing neighbor would call in for a moment. Sometimes leaving a bunch of flowers and sometimes a prayer that God would support me in my affliction. One dark night there came up a very great storm of wind and rain. The lightning flashed constantly and the thunder shook my cabin until I certainly thought it would fall down. Being all alone my fears were great. But all at once a light, beautiful and soft, filled all the room, and I thought I heard a voice whisper, saying, "Be not afraid, I am with thee, thou shalt not be afraid of the terror by night." Suddenly I seemed to see the presence of shining ones in my room. I sat up in my bed and said, "Oh, Lord, art

Thou here?" and repeated a word from the prophet. "I will trust and not be afraid, for the Lord Jehovah is my strength and my song." (Isaiah 12:2) All the remainder of that night I was filled with praises to God. My soul was exceedingly happy."

Just then the angel who had been talking with us, smilingly said: "I know all about that night and was present with you. I was present also at your bedside the night you died and strengthened your soul that your trust might be perfect until you were released, and my co-charioteer yonder brought you safely to the portals of paradise." Just at this moment she began to praise God again for her great deliverance, and I said to myself again, "surely those who had the poorest and hardest fare in the world are happiest now."

We have lingered long enough just for a glance at the surroundings outside the city walls. I must hasten on to what was within, for the great attractions were inside.

"But," said Seneca, I cannot describe to you these wonders tonight, for you are already weary." So saying, he bade me good night and was gone.

CHAPTER NINE

Sixth Visit
Entering in Through the Gate — Welcomed by the Lord Jesus

The sun was just setting when Seneca came again. I was on my knees in prayer, and as I opened my eyes he was standing by my side.

"I greet you again tonight, my son," he said, "and with God's blessing upon you, we will now proceed with the narrative." He commenced by saying:

We were nearing the great gateway. Every one of the new arrivals was filled with wonder and anxiety. We had heard so much about the Holy City while we lived in the world, of its many mansions, its streets of gold, its gates of pearl, its transparent light without sun or moon, so that we all felt an intense yearning to enter in. But the greatest attraction of all was to see Him whom our souls loved and by whom we had been redeemed and by whose blood we had been washed from our sins. We had already been told that He was waiting near the gate in one of the mansions and that the great Book of Life would be near Him and be opened to the pages bearing our names. This filled us with great anxiety; although we felt a sweet assurance that our names were there, and that we would receive His gracious welcome. Yes we felt sure or we never would have been carried by the angels into paradise, were it not so. For we had confessed Him on earth and we knew He had already confessed us before His Father and the angels. This gave us comfort; and then we knew we had been eating of the tree of life and drinking of the crystal river, so with confidence we kept looking forward. We knew we had been trying to please Him, and the conscious sense that all our sin had been forgiven and our robes washed and made white, was additional consolation to us now. We felt we would soon stand before the judge of all the earth.

God's Word seemed further comfort where He says, "Blessed are they that do His commandments, that they may have right to the tree of life, and may enter in through the gates into the city." (Revelation 22:14) We felt such a comfort in this assurance, that if we had a right to the tree of life, and the

36

fruit given us was by an elder's hand, and that Abraham himself had refreshed and immortalized us from the river of God which came from the throne itself, that the angel at the gate would not debar us entering now. Just at this time my mother, who had been busily engaged in conversation with others, came to me and said:

"You need have no fears. It gave me much joy when many years ago I was passing near where the angel was recording the names of those who had been born again, and seeing your name I at once asked the angel who it was. He called another angel who had just come from the scenes of earthly conflict, where they were having great religious awakenings, and asked him if he could tell who these were whose names were just written. "Oh," he said, "I have just been among them," and described everything so minutely that I had all assurance it was you. Then other names which I saw registered were from the same place. My old home, our old home. Indeed the memory of it is dear to me as I think of it now. We will talk over the details of it some day; as things have been since I left you all. My soul was filled with exceeding great joy when I saw your name. Then the angel told me when he found I was your mother, that he went with you and your cousin, whom I knew so well, one night as you went from the scenes of prayer and stood by your side late at night, while you solemnly made a vow and pledged faithfulness to God and to each other, that he went and woke your father who was sleeping in another room and led him out to witness your covenant. Oh, you may know that not only I, but the angels rejoiced with me when they brought me the tidings. He also told me of the conversion of other members of our family, and many more in the neighborhood.

"Well, well," I said, "does heaven have such communications as these with the affairs of the world?" How little we seemed to know it! Yet my mother's words brought up all this past experience. The scenes of my conversion, midnight prayers, earnest labor for others, the events she just alluded to with many others all came rushing through my mind and the memory was fresh as though but yesterday.

I said, "How blind I was not to see the angel who was with me. The mighty veil of mortality, how it blinds the eye of man from spiritual beings and things! How far away they seem to be and yet how very near! I remembered how angels assisted Lot

37

and his family from the condemned city of Sodom, and why should they not assist in the soul's great struggle after salvation! For I remember "they are all ministering spirits sent forth to minister for those who shall be heirs of salvation."

By this time we were entering the massive Judean gateway. Our hearts were all filled with joy in the expectation of so soon seeing Him whom our souls loved. As we passed through the gateway the most beautiful scene met our gaze that we had ever witnessed before in heaven or on earth. Human language cannot describe it. To say the streets were pure gold or transparent glass would give the best idea by way of comparison of any object I know. The great thoroughfares leading from the gate seemed to lead off toward the center of the Holy City. On the right hand as we passed in were mighty, stupendous columns of precious stone shining with a brightness that heaven only knows. Massive domes and great archways were overhead. Nothing showed any signs of decay or age. No rubbish or signs of wear. The light toward the mansion was exceeding great. Our Lord now came forward to meet and welcome us. Twelve legions of happy souls had now filed in at the great gateway and stood before our King. The glory and majesty of His being can never be described. The beloved disciple on Patmos once tried to tell of His glorious appearance as He revealed Himself on earth; He was then clothed with a flowing garment down to His feet and girt about with a golden girdle; His head and hair seemed white as snow, and His eyes as a flame of fire; His feet were glowing like burnished brass; His countenance was like the sun at midday; a sharp two-edged sword was in His mouth and seven stars were in His right hand. (Revelation 1:13-16) But when the disciples saw Him on the Mount of Transfiguration sixty-three years before, His garments then shone as the light and His face with the brilliancy of the sun. On earth He was called the fairest among ten thousand and altogether lovely. But as He is now in His exaltation in heaven, the language is too tame to express His glory. He bore the marks in His hands, and above His sandals the nail prints showed distinctly. He was the very embodiment of light. It was not dazzling to our eyes as was Moses' face to Israel of old, for we were prepared for it: since the days of our conversion on earth until we passed through this gate we were being prepared for this vision of our Lord. Oh, how forcibly were the words of Scripture as I looked

38

upon His face and then glanced far into the city! "And the city had no need of the sun, neither of the moon, for the glory of God did lighten it and the Lamb is the light thereof." He was also the embodiment of love itself. Every feature of His face spoke of love. Indeed it was the reflection of His Father's infinite love. All the love in heaven or in the church on earth came from Him. He bade us welcome to Him, and as we came, by one mighty impulse we all fell on our faces and began to worship Him with adoring praise, saying, "Worthy is the Lamb that was slain and has redeemed us to God by thy blood out of every kindred and tongue and people and nation." The angels and the saints who met us, also joined and sang some new songs which we had never heard before. Our souls were in ecstasies of joy not to be described.

How long we remained upon our faces we could not tell for our gladness, joys and great satisfaction were so deep and blessed we took no note of eternity's register. He now addressed us in most loving words, giving us His cordial welcome and confessing us before the multitude of angels present, and to His Father's face, and without further introduction we felt perfectly acquainted.

"Come," said He, "look into this book. I have opened it to the pages most interesting to you."

We all gathered around Him in turns as closely as we could, to look upon the pages of the great book of books, the heavenly records of the past and future.

Not only were our names written, but underneath them were many things bearing upon our work for God while in the earth. I then remembered what God had said by one of His prophets which I read a hundred times over. That a "book of remembrance was written before Him for them that thought upon His name: and they shall be mine, saith the Lord of hosts, in that day when I make up my jewels." (Malachi 3:16,17)

We only took time to read a tithe of what was written, for our Lord said: "You now have perfect liberty to go where you will and to read at your leisure the contents of this most wonderful book." In glancing over its pages we noticed the names of some who were with us when we first entered paradise, who had fallen back in the rear and remained far outside the gates of pearl. Without any further words of explanation we knew that they were not prepared, but were like

39

the ancient high priest when unsanctified, unworthy of the altar, so these could not serve around the throne. Yet we knew they would be brought in, for they were somewhere along the river of life and among the trees whose fruit was their food and whose leaves were for their healing. Their present reward was all that God could give them with their present stage of grace. These leaves, we knew, were only for those whose names were in the Book of Life and that they have the same healing power in them that the sanctifying grace of God had in His kingdom on earth. The remedy indeed was around them, but they would not receive it. They never realized the deep meaning of the precious sacrifice for them; but how thankful to know that the efficacy of His blood availeth for those of His people on this side of the river as well as on that. We knew also that much of our redemption is yet to follow and will be realized at the resurrection morning of the great day.

I had often wondered if we should have knowledge of the lost ones and should miss any of our friends from the Holy City, if we would not be filled with sadness and grief, although God had said, "All tears should be wiped away." (Revelation 21:4) But now I found it was all settled. I had been there long enough to pass the river of life, drink of its crystal waters, eat of the fruit of the trees upon its banks, and be greeted by thousands of the blood-washed from the chariots of God, beside entering in at the gates, and during all this time only the highest emotions of praise filled my soul. I was so completely in God's love, and my own will was so lost in the conscious will of my blessed Redeemer, that I had never thought once of weeping about anything. In fact, I found that all my faculties and dispositions to sorrow and sadness were gone and I now could see things as God sees them.

And then as I stood beside my Redeemer and Lord, and the great Book of Life lay open before me, and I could see far into the city and could see multitudes of happy souls whom I had not met nor did I know who they might be, some I did not know, but some whom I had known on earth and had feared were among the lost might be here in the city, and especially since I had been greeted by some whom I never expected to see in heaven. And in looking over the pages of the Book of Life I saw the names of many whom I thought would not be there, and I knew they must be somewhere in the great city or in the vast domains of the paradise of God.

I now felt anxious to go on and mingle with the happy souls which I saw passing in all directions. The Lord had said: "You have entire liberty. Go where you will." I turned to see the rest of our legions, for I had been so enraptured by what I saw and heard, that I had tarried long; but to my surprise they had scattered in many directions; some had gone with their friends to quiet places, and beneath the trees, they were sitting on the upholstery of heaven in joyous conversation; others, meeting with old friends, had boarded the chariots and with them gone to distant places of the city.

My mother was still near me and beckoned me to come with her. We walked only a short distance and sat down beside a stupendous column of what seemed jasper and sapphire, shining with the light which the eternal city only knows. The cushions were of the finest fabric, and the upholstering had been done by the hands of saints and angels, for everyone is busily employed in heaven. Compulsion is not known, but contentment of which we only knew the shadow while in our most restful moments in earth, seemed to clothe everyone here as a garment.

At this Seneca Sodi stood up and said: "My son, I will see you again at the appointed time. The blessings of God Almighty be upon you, and among these blessings cause His face to shine upon you and give you rest." I looked up from my writing only to see him vanishing from my room.

CHAPTER TEN

Seventh Visit
Visit with His Mother

My visitor was here on time and the following was his message:

I now turned to my mother and said: "I have been wanting a private talk with you for some time. It does seem so good to be here with you. It seems like a very short time since I sat upon your knee and you told me the story of our future home. How little I comprehended the reality of it! But we are safe in the city now and I want to ask you some questions about our home here, our privileges and duties."

"Be perfectly free to ask any questions you like. We learn of the wonders of our Father's house, just as we did on earth by applying ourselves to all the means and sources of knowledge."

"I want to know first what privileges we have here in heaven, both in the city and outside in paradise and elsewhere, and what are the laws that govern these privileges and our conduct?"

"I understand fully," she said, "what you want to know. You have asked some very important questions and I am glad to assist you with any detailed explanations you wish."

"Your privileges, however, are unbounded. Your capacities for pleasure and enjoyment are greatly enlarged since leaving the scenes of your earthly life. Everything here invites the fullest exercise of every faculty of your soul. Your conduct will be governed by a knowledge of God's will. You will never wish to do anything or exercise yourself contrary to the will of God.

"The law of love and light is the law of the heavenly kingdom. No one wishes to do anything here which would not be morally right. There is no thought or suggestion by anyone, of himself or another doing anything morally wrong. You have found, no doubt, ere this that you have no inclinations within yourself or temptation from without to do any wrong thing. Everything that you feel inclined to do is right, so far as moral right is concerned. Your knowledge is yet limited. Whatever God approves and your knowledge comprehends you will approve from the innermost depths of your soul. His will be-

42

comes law to you. He never charges guilt upon anyone here, for no one in all this heavenly kingdom has any feelings or wish to disobey. Sin is not known here. That great curse of the earth is entirely banished from these streets and mansions of the city; from the drives, walks and resorts of paradise as well. No stain of sin has ever been here since God cast out the angels who sinned. Every one of those thousands whom you see yonder coming and going are the image of God so completely that they have no desire to do otherwise than just to fulfill His will. Our duty here is only a blessed privilege. It is our great delight to do all we ought to do. Restraint and compulsion, of which I remember we knew so much in the earth, are words which have no meaning here. You have noticed, no doubt, ere this, that everyone you have met or seen has been perfectly joyful and happy. Discontent is unknown here. Everyone is altogether satisfied and entirely at rest."

"Oh, how wonderfully grand this is!" I replied, "but I should like to know further, if I do not weary you with my questions, what privileges we have here in heaven, by way of going from place to place, and visiting among the beautiful mansions I see lining those great avenues and thoroughfares of the city. Our Lord has said, "Go where you will, enjoy yourselves.""

"Oh!" she said, smilingly, "go just where you please. All that you see and infinitely more are yours — yes, all are yours. Do you not remember that Scripture: "All are yours, and ye are Christ's and Christ is God's?" (I Corinthians 3:22,23) I have been here for over sixty years and I have gone multitudes of times to distant parts of the city, and yet I have seen but a little portion of my inheritance. Speaking in language which you will better understand, the city is fifteen hundred miles each way and its height is the same as its length and breadth. (Revelation 21:16,17) So its vastness is sufficient for you and you have the privileges of it all."

"Oh, my mother! How wonderful are the works of God! I am simply lost in admiration and wonder!"

"Indeed," said she, "your wonder will never come to an end. Story upon story is built and the inconceivable height and glory and vastness can never be fully comprehended by us. You see those fountains yonder gushing with their pure water of life?"

"Yes," I replied, "I have been noticing them for quite a while and wanted to ask you concerning them, for I see so many gathering about them and drinking from golden goblets. I presume they are free for all?"

"Indeed, and they are throughout the city and even to the remotest parts of paradise. Do you remember the Scripture which I used to read to you near seventy years ago, that the "Lamb which is in the midst of the throne shall feed them and shall lead them unto living fountains of waters"? (Revelation 7:17)

"Sure enough, I have read it hundreds of times since, but I never thought it meant so much."

"But when you get to the throne itself you will see the greatness of its meaning as you cannot now. You have already eaten of the trees of life, and drank of the crystal river, I am sure, for you have that privilege immediately on coming into the border lands of heaven; but did you notice there were twelve kinds of fruit on each tree?" (Revelation 22:2)

"Yes, so the elder told me. I have eaten only a very few times since entering paradise; and others have selected for me. Those lovely trees in the midst of the street, how full of fruit they are!"

"They were all planted and are growing by the immediate direction of our Lord Himself," said mother. "You remember His words while on earth "I go to prepare a place for you," (John 14:2) and here it is. Those fountains and trees with all their blessings are forever yours. One never tires of anything he has here, nor wishes for anything that he cannot have. The varieties of food are so abundant you can eat and be wholly satisfied."

Just at this moment we saw one not far away, whom among the thousands we distinguished as one of the elders. I said to mother: "Would he mind stopping for a short visit with us? What do you think?"

"No doubt he would be pleased to do so." So she beckoned him to come to us. As he was coming toward us she said: "Oh, it is Moses, sure."

"How thankful I am," I replied, "for I have been wishing to see him ever since we entered paradise." But as he came nearer I felt something of an awe coming over me as I remembered his greatness while on earth. I also felt a fear that the questions which I wished to ask him might not interest him since, as I thought, he had been asked the same a thousand times.

"You need not fear," said mother, "to ask him any questions you like, for he will take great pleasure in assisting you in any way he can."

Meeting a group at one of the fountains nearby, he was detained for a time, in conversation with them. While waiting for him, I said: "I remember in the Scriptures it is said, "There are twenty-four elders in heaven.""

"Yes," said mother, "twelve from former dispensations and twelve since the days of Christ."

I asked if there were the same distinctions and reverence shown here as on earth.

"Quite the same," said she, "only on a true basis — for past fidelity and merit. The elders are greatly honored here in heaven. They have already had their resurrection which gives them superior advantages for enjoyment and service and yet their bodies are so spiritual that instead of being a hindrance to them they are a very great help and advantage. You have noticed, no doubt, how wonderfully they are in the likeness of the Lord Himself."

"I have noticed that already in what I have seen in Abraham and Joshua, and I now remember that Scripture where the prophet said: "I shall be satisfied when I awake in thy likeness." (Psalm 17:15)

"Indeed," said mother, "and we are all looking toward that event with great interest. No doubt you have heard since your coming that the Lord has intimated that the time has nearly come when the general resurrection will take place. When you and I and all these multitudes of souls shall have our spiritual bodies. The great Father Himself, whose spirit you so abundantly feel and which is the very atmosphere of the city and all paradise, has made us all to feel and know that the time is nearly here. There are some events to occur upon earth first, and then our Lord Jesus accompanied with all the angels and this mighty host of redeemed spirits made perfect, will descend to the earth, the order will be that when we are near the earth where our bodies are sleeping (for what we used to call death is only a sleep), that the archangel will give a great shout of victory and the trumpet of God will be blown with a mighty blast and the power of God will awaken and revive all our bodies and they will instantly spring from the dust and with a mighty change will be made spiritual and we will instantly be united with them and be forever in the perfect image of Jesus, and the last stroke of our redemption will be completed."

"Oh!" I replied. "How wonderful is the plan of our redemption! God has given us, I remember, the same idea of what you have been saying as recorded in the New Testament Scripture."

"Yes," said mother, "and this is the hope and expectation of all the church in heaven and on earth. But I see Moses is now coming to us and we will have to leave further conversation on this subject until another time."

CHAPTER ELEVEN

Seventh Visit — Continued
Visit with Moses

By this time he had come to us, and with a friendly greeting we shook hands and my mother gave us an introduction. He very cordially welcomed me, and in a moment all my feelings of backwardness at meeting with such an honored and favored servant of God as he had been and was were gone. The grace with which he met me and the welcome he gave caused an immediate yearning in me to be near him. I felt I could lean my head with great joy on his bosom.

The meekness so characteristic of his nature while on earth clothed every feature of his soul now. He did not seem like a man who had lived one hundred twenty years on the earth under such great burdens of responsibilities as he had passed through. There were no marks of age, or wrinkles or any oldish looking appearance about him. Only his hair and beard were of flaxen whiteness. He was rather above the average in stature, and his robes were white as snow. He stood quite erect and had a most imposing dignity and yet so gentle and lovely that my soul loved him exceedingly at once.

My mother and he entered into a short conversation about a number of children who were just outside the gate, and asked me to excuse their conversation a moment. I heard him ask her if she would go and assist them in the knowledge and ways of the heavenly kingdom. We were so near the gateway, that we could distinctly hear them singing and could discern the voices — very sweet and angelic. Mother said she would be quite glad to go and spend some time among them and teach them of heavenly things. So turning to Moses she said:

"My son would be pleased for a short visit with you, as he has only recently entered the city." "I shall be much pleased also," said Moses, "for to assist and help each other is much of our occupation in heaven as you know yourself." Whereupon my mother made a gentle bow, adding the words, "I'll see you again," and waving a good-bye with her hand she was gone.

Moses now said: "You were fortunate to have had such a mother on earth. She is greatly esteemed in heaven, and very much used in the service of her Lord. But I see, my son, you are very full of questions and the inquiries and investigations of your soul are of great service to you here. Let us walk to yonder cluster of trees and take some fruit that we may be eating while we are talking. I always enjoyed the social and religious feasts while on earth, and it remains with me still. I greatly enjoy eating with my friends." He selected from the different kinds what we wanted and said as he handed me a bunch of what seemed like large transparent grapes. These will help you in understanding the mystery of the kingdom of God — mysteries not so much connected with our redemption as our further development in heaven and growth in a knowledge of His will for the great future."

"There have been great discussions of recent years," I said to Moses, "over some portions of the Scripture, especially of the book of Genesis which you wrote, what was meant and what time embraced in the six days of creation, and the seventh day in which it is said, "God rested." I used to say if ever I got to heaven I would see Moses and ask about these things. And at last, here we are, face to face."

"Well," said Moses, my time and knowledge are at your disposal. I have been asked very similar questions hundreds of times. But just one word of explanation will make it all clear to you. In the first place, to begin back of where I began when writing under the inspiration of God, before the beginning the great cycles of eternity knew nothing of the earth. It was known only in the mind of God, and long before He laid the foundations of the earth, He thought of each of us. But this beginning and each successive day of creation were long periods of time. Each cycle was called a day which measured a vast period of creation under infinite laws. The same laws were in operation as they are now, God's will was simply His law. When He said, "Let the dry land appear," ages were occupied in developing the continents for our earthly home, and so period after period, the work was done and the earth was populated with creation of His own will. Great events are in store for the earth yet. The restitution of all things has not occurred yet. God shall cleanse, change and remodel it again by fire. His voice shall yet shake the earth as it has never been shaken. He shall prepare it for a suitable place for His bride in the great wedding tour which we will yet take. Do you not remember His Word, written long after my day: "Whose voice then shook the earth, but now He hath promised saying, Yet once more I shake not the earth only but also heaven"? (Hebrews 12:26) The renovation of the earth and the removing out of His kingdom there all things which offend and do iniquity is another great day yet to come, and nearly here. All the wise ones of earth will be ready and waiting for it.

"Well," I said to Moses, "I am deeply interested in these great matters of creation, but may we not leave them for another visit for there are other things which I wish to ask you about."

"Certainly," said Moses.

"Tell me something concerning our Lord Jesus, ere He was born in the world and became our sacrifice for sin."

"Well, " said Moses, "He was always one with the Father. He was truly the Word of God. The creative energy of the almighty Jehovah. Without Him God did nothing. "Let us make" was an expression common in all the works and creations of God. His title always was the "Word," and until He was born on earth He was not known as the Son, but as the Word only. He has been present in the creation of the world, and was and is the glory of the Father's throne in this celestial kingdom. But it was a great event in heaven when the announcement was made that Jesus was born in Bethlehem. It was the most exciting occasion ever witnessed in all the heavenly domain. All the angels tuned their harps, for the Lord said, "Let all the angels of God worship Him." I have seen great times on earth when the millions of Israel all joined in the chorus of praise at the passage of the Red Sea, and when all the great hosts rushed from their tents at the sounding of the trumpet of God on Mount Sinai; but never was anything equal to this. Multitudes of angels at once descended to where the infant Jesus was; but no such worship or music has ever been heard in heaven. Everything throughout all the streets and avenues of the city and even to the utmost bounds of paradise the voice of thanksgiving was being poured forth to God. The angels were not alone in this praise, for all of us who had come from the earth knew that our salvation was through Him who had just been born into the world and you may know we all joined with them in one prolonged praise to God. It was an event which had been pondered with anxiety by all the heavenly host for long ages past."

"Thank God," I said to Moses, "for His birth. And I now remember a passage of the blessed word of the Lord bearing on this same subject: "Of which salvation the prophets have enquired and searched diligently who prophesied of the grace that should come unto you. Searching what or what manner of time, the Spirit of God which was in them did signify when it testified beforehand the sufferings of Christ and the glory that should follow: Unto whom it was revealed that not unto themselves, but unto us, they did minister the things which are now reported unto you, by them that have preached the gospel unto you with the Holy Ghost sent down from heaven, which things the angels desire to look into." (I Peter 1:10-12)

"You are right, my son," said Moses, "and we all knew that the world's redemption was connected with His birth, life and death. The angels were in constant attendance upon Him at all times and brought us detailed accounts of all that occurred in His life. Many things of which I am told there is no record upon earth are faithfully written in the Book of Life, a volume of which is at each of the twelve gates and the angel always has it in charge. If you desire," said Moses, "we will walk at once to the Judean gateway, which is not far from here and see some of the things written therein."

I said to him: "I entered at that gate only a short time ago and saw the book and glanced over a few of its pages and should be much pleased to look into it again, for our Lord said, "You can all read at your leisure." As we were going, Moses said to me: "Did the book equal your expectations?" "Oh," I said, "it far exceeded them. It is so large and grand, yet it seemed easily handled, for everything in heaven seems to be of such a spiritual character."

He quickly turned to that portion bearing the title: "Records of the Son of God." As he slowly turned the leaves I glanced at the various headings bearing on the many events in His most wonderful life. It was exceedingly interesting and precious to notice with what wonderful harmony the records of His life were given in the Scriptures and in this blessed book of all books. It seemed more interesting still, since I knew that one had been written by the instrumentality of man and the other by the hand of angels. The angels know all about our language and have witten all things intelligible to us. The angels whom Jacob saw in his dream ascending and descending upon

50

the ladder, bearing confirmations of the covenant given to Abraham were the same who were in constant attendance upon the Son of God during His wonderful incarnate life upon earth, and watched every detail of His life, and much of it has been faithfully written. I read with fresh interest the account of His birth, of the special illumination by the guiding star given to the wise men of the east, in the language of the Record: "A light from heaven guided them to the place where the world's Redeemer was born." Of Herod's miserable attempt to destroy Him by killing all the young children of those parts, and of his continued and determined wrath against Him until an angel brought his life to an end.

As he turned the pages I noticed many accounts of His early life not given in the Scriptures. One especially attracted my attention, the title was: "Jesus Taught by the Father." The event seemed to occur when He was but five years old. Joseph had gone from home and the child Jesus was left alone in His father's place of business, His mother being busy in the house. Suddenly a bright cloud filled all that mechanic's room. The Father Himself overshadowed and held conversation with Him, telling Him who He was: that God was His Father, and communicated to Him much concerning His earthly mission. "All this," said Moses, "he knew as God, but as He was man also He learned by being taught."

Another account was written: "Caught Up to Paradise." It was during the night while all were asleep that He was caught up to the paradise of God and was with the Father for many hours in which the Father said to Him: "Thou art man as well as God for Thou wast born of a woman. All power and authority shall soon be given into Thy hands; and Thou shalt lay down Thy life for the salvation of men." I then quickly remembered His own words: "This commandment I have received from my Father." (John 10:18) "Thou shalt also prepare and fix up mansions in this upper kingdom for Thy future home and that of all Thy children for they shall be many."

Before morning had broken upon the earth, angels had conducted Him safely to His home at Nazareth and before any stir by servants or parents He was in His room in prayer.

"Now," said Moses, "this incarnate life of Jesus on earth was made necessary on account of man's sin and rebellion against God. No other method was ever devised for our salvation. You can look further into the book if you like, and at any time you wish."

CHAPTER TWELVE

Seventh Visit – Continued
Further Visit with Moses

"These accounts," I replied, "are exceedingly interesting. I have often said while on earth that many things we did not know nor could know, we would know hereafter."

"True enough," said Moses. "The fact is, we only just began to know the first rudiments of the knowledge of God while on earth."

"I suppose that would be true of the large mass of mankind whose knowledge is so limited concerning divine things, but you seem to include yourself along with the rest of us, and it seems a little strange since you were for so many years in such intimate fellowship with God – talked face to face with Him – saw His glory so often, were His special friend so long."

"I know," said Moses, "that God did highly favor me, but it was for your sakes as much as my own; but after all, since I came into the heavenly kingdom and into His immediate presence about the throne, I find I know but little of what is evidently yet to be known. God revealed much of Himself to me, as I thought, but that much was only a tithe of the great mysteries of His eternal nature, wisdom and works. Even as regards our common salvation, the angels who for long ages have been about the throne, are yet eager to learn. "Here," said Moses, "is a page you would like to see, I am sure. It is one of the great events in the earlier life of Jesus, not recorded in the Holy Scriptures on earth." The headlines were: **"The mission of Jesus more fully confirmed by the Father."** The event occurred when He was about twenty-two years of age. He had retired to a distant mountain to pray and was all alone, except many of the angels were about Him, when the Father in a most extraordinary manner met with Him and reiterated in fullness of meaning all that had been revealed by the shadows of the law. The Father spoke of His death to be accomplished at Jerusalem and of its vicarious nature. How His death was to be for all men and showed Him the fullness of His love for the world, and that His sufferings and death should be the price of the world's redemption, and that His death should be the great atonement for the salvation of man. The account also showed how He should die and the fearful sorrows of the occasion: His rejection by the Jews, His scourging and final death on the cross. Reference was also made of His resurrection and ascension into heaven. "All these things," said Moses, "Jesus as the Word always knew; but as the Son of God, He was instructed by the Father, and did fully His will in all His incarnate life on earth."

Very many things I saw written there of the occurrences in His life most interesting to me now. "Oh, yes," I replied to Moses as he turned the pages, "I remember how John the beloved disciple said as he finished his narrative of the Son of God: 'And there are many other things which Jesus did, the which if they should be written every one, I suppose that even the world itself could not contain the books that should be written.' " (John 21:25)

I asked Moses why these are written here instead of in the records on earth.

"These," he replied, "are for the satisfaction and comfort of God's children in heaven."

"Well, well," I remarked, "I am lost in wonder and surprise. But, father Moses," I said, "you had a most remarkable experience in the days of our Lord while on earth. The Scriptures make reference to the transfiguration of Jesus on the Holy Mount and that He took Peter, James and John with Him and that you and Elias came also and were talking with Him concerning His death."

"Yes," said Moses, "I look back to that event with great pleasure. At the time the hosts of Israel were ready to cross the Jordan into the land of their inheritance I was very anxious to go over with them; but God thought it not best, and His will is always right. I did not then know that He meant to answer my prayer after so many long years had passed – that is, long years as regards earthly count – it was only a day and a half of heaven's measure."

"That was a great day when the Lord beckoned us to the earth. All powers had just been given into His hands both in heaven and in earth. I cannot fully describe to you our feelings when Elias and myself were walking together near the throne talking of the great event so soon to occur in the earth, and its great meaning both to earth and heaven. I was speaking of His tragic death soon to be accomplished on the cross, and he of the blessed gift of the Holy Ghost to be offered to all God's children on the earth; for our great mission and concern had been to unfold these two features of the work of the Son of God.

We had enjoyed many precious visits and much conversation about these questions when unexpectedly Michael, one of the chief angels, whom possibly you have seen, and Jehuco, the swift charioteer, brought a chariot to our side and said that we were called for immediately to the earth. Without further preparations we were quickly seated by their side and, with almost the rapidity of thought, we were flying through the great avenues and passed out of the city at the gate of Manasseh. The vast plains, mountains and valleys of paradise were quickly passed. We were so enraptured with the thought of a visit to earth we hardly knew what to say nor had we time to say it until we were slowing up somewhere in the regions of a terrestrial sphere. In a moment more, its cities, towns, mountains and rivers were visible to us. Just at this moment Michael said to Jehuco, "Slacken thy speed still more and drive the chariot past Mount Nebo." I cried out and said, "Oh, Michael, thou blessed servant of God. Are we so near the land of my earthly pilgrimage, and to the mount where my last earthly prayer was offered and where I laid aside the veil of my flesh? I am so glad to see old Nebo again. My body was laid away somewhere here." "Yes," said Michael, "we know all about it and where it is. I will speak unto thee again, later on about it, but now we must hasten on." In a moment more the chariot wheels were standing still on Olivet's summit, and we had stepped upon the earth which had been the scenes of my former life and within the promised land to which I had led the hosts of Israel, and longed to enter it myself, and now my prayer was answered after many hundreds of years had passed.

CHAPTER THIRTEEN

Seventh Visit — Continued
Moses' Description of the Transfiguration

Moses continued and said: "Only a short distance from us was a bright cloud suspended a little way above, but really it was settling down upon the mount. It reminded me very much of the cloud that went before us in the wilderness and led the hosts of Israel in their journeys. We quickly left the chariot and the angels standing by its side, and proceeded to the place over which the cloud hung. As we came near we had the first glimpse of Him who was both God and man. He had clothed Himself in the livery of heaven for the occasion. We found Him on His knees in prayer and somewhat hidden behind some low shrubbery. The three disciples were kneeling near Him, but were so overcome with the glory that they seemed asleep. He arose and met us with a most cordial greeting, and the place was so resplendent with glory that it seemed we might have been still about the throne itself. It did seem passing strange to think we were upon the earth again. We knew the time had arrived when He should become the great sacrifice for the world's redemption. I had foreshadowed Him by the manifold shadows of the law. Indeed, I saw something of His majesty and the glory of His kingdom when in a figure God made my face to shine like the sun on Mount Sinai, with which, no doubt, you are familiar, for it was faithfully written." (Exodus 34:29)

"Oh! I remember it quite well," I replied, "and have often made reference to it as typifying the beauty of moral character."

"Very true," said Moses, "but it also foreshadowed the transfiguration scene and the future period yet to come, and which, we are informed, is near at hand, when the millennial glory of Christ is to appear upon the earth and all the saints shall share in the glory, a glimpse of which was seen on the Holy Mount.

"We stood united in our testimony to the Son of God. But after we had been called away the three disciples saw no man but Jesus only. The great Father spoke out of the cloud and declared this was His only beloved Son, well pleasing to Him. We had much conversation with Him on the great themes of sacrifice and atonement, the Holy Spirit, and the plan of man's redemption. The church now has ample proof of His divinity and can fully trust in the great sacrifice which He has made.

"Our Lord spoke as familiarly to me as though we had been intimately acquainted for hundreds of years, and indeed He had been during much of my earthly life and toil, my constant friend. He was the "Angel of the Covenant," and was in the cloud which went before and followed us in our journeys in the wilderness. Long before His incarnation in the flesh He was the light of heaven and was with His church on earth. He gave us a cordial introduction to the disciples with whom we had converse.

"When He had dismissed us, the chariot drove to our side, and in a few moments we said good-bye, and leaving Olivet's summit were on our homeward trip. Michael now turned to me and said: 'Would you like to go past the cave?' 'I should be greatly delighted,' I replied, 'will you please stop a moment at its threshold?'

"When the chariot stood still, Michael, Elias and myself stepped out. Michael now said, 'No man has known where your body was laid until this day. The Lord directed a secret burial, lest the people of Israel should worship your remains. The devil contended for a long time that we should give it a public burial. But you are aware that we are now at the place? Your body was laid far back in a cave that used to be here. After it had been laid to rest, we touched the rocks and they came down and filled the entrance and here it has been sleeping ever since." At this I humbly bowed myself before God and blessed Him for His promise of the resurrection.

"We now hastily ascended to the top of Pisgah and once again I was standing where I had stood nearly sixteen hundred years before. Oh, how fresh the memories of it all were! Everything came back to me."

I had been so entranced by this remarkable story, that I almost thought myself on the earth again, but turning to Moses, I said: "How wonderful are the dealings of God to the children of men! What great things are in store for them!"

"Surely," said Moses, "but I must finish my narrative. Just here Michael said, "We must hasten on." Seated again in the chariot he said to his charioteer, "Go past Bethlehem, for there are two souls just released which we must take with us." The

56

chariot seemed to go with the rapidity of the lightning. We received the two souls and were soaring to the regions above and toward the gateways of paradise. When we had stepped out, Elias remained with them for further instruction, and I was soon once more at the throne.

"I see," said Moses, "that we have been standing here a long time and you will have ample time to look into this book at your leisure."

"I am thankful for that, "I replied, "and shall often avail myself of the privilege."

Moses now said: "You have not been far into the city, nor about the throne, have you?"

"No, but I am anxious to go, if I only had someone to go with me as a guide. There were many who entered the city at the same time I did, but they have all disappeared among the countless hosts I see in every direction."

"You have taken a wise course, my son. Get acquainted as you go along. There are many who will lend you all the assistance you require. I see you are anxious to see your mother again, she will return to you soon and you can enjoy her association as you will."

"I thank you very much for your kindness, Father Moses, and will improve the opportunities as they come to me."

Moses then said, "I hope to see you again soon, and at the throne if not before," and with a pleasant word of blessing he said good-bye.

I turned about only to see my friend Bohemond coming toward me. We had parted at the Judean gate and had not met since. So we went to a quiet place and sat down to talk over the things of our wonderful visits and experiences."

CHAPTER FOURTEEN

Eighth Visit
Great Prayer Meeting in Heaven

Seneca Sodi came early. The usual greetings passed between us and he began as follows:

Bohemond and I now walked a short distance to a most remarkable cluster of buildings which Moses had just pointed out to me. They were massive, stupendous, and grand. They occupied one whole block of the city and seemed to be four-square. A great inscription was written above the threshold: "Treasures Laid Up in Heaven."

We spent a long time going from place to place looking into these wonderful treasures, which God's people have secured for themselves, as well as rejected blessings which might have been secured by a diligent effort while on earth, for we found that all these multitudes of holy gems, jewels, pearls and lovely garments all had their counterpart in the experience of saints on earth. These heavenly jewels might have been easily secured and would have added much to the riches of the soul in the heavenly kingdom. But I can tell you more of these at another time. Before leaving the shrine of holy symbols we were told that not far away from here was a place where great congregations meet for public worship and praise, many hundreds of which are located in different parts of the Holy City. I said to Bohemond, "Let us go there at once for we have enjoyed no congregational worship since leaving the Judean gate."

As we stepped out at the door of the sacred shrine onto the opened street we found it was literally crowded with thousands of happy souls on their way to the great praise service. "Oh, listen," I said to Bohemond, "to the strains of music." It seemed far in the distance and yet we could hear it quite distinctly.

"Oh," he replied to me, "it must be the orchestra of heaven."

"Indeed, I think it is, and I am anxious to be among them." I spoke to one of the many who were thronging the streets and who seemed to be perfectly acquainted with the surroundings, asking if he could tell about the order of the service and the chances of a convenient place.

"To be sure," said he, "every comfort is provided. Have you not attended the service before?"

"This is our first, as we have just lately come into the city."

"Then you will be welcomed and ushered to a more prominent place, so you will have better opportunities of learning the worship of heaven. All the strangers are brought forward and introduced to the great multitudes and given favored places. So you will be entirely free and easy."

We thanked him for his kindness and felt a sense of relief.

Just at this point came two chariots sweeping along in which were seated many of the patriarchs, prophets, and apostles of Jesus. I noticed that each of them had a harp, and someone with a large stringed instrument stood up prominently among them. I said, "Who is the man with his face shining with such glory, having the stringed instrument?"

Several spoke at once and said: You have sung his hymns and Psalms a thousand times. Guess who he is."

I did not need to be told. I knew it was David the King. Anticipating my desires someone beckoned to the charioteer. David also called us to come and sit with him. We were soon by his side and the chariot was rolling along with noiseless but slackened speed. I said to David and the rest, as I turned toward my friend: "This is Bohemond from Northern Russia whom I met at my first introduction into paradise. I am from the opposite side of the earth, and although our homes were so remote from each other, yet we are brethren in the Lord."

"We are glad to welcome you, my sons, to the Holy City, and also into this chariot, said David. "Of course, you are going where we all are going, up to join the great congregation in the worship and praise of our Redeemer."

"Indeed we are and shall be glad to go along with you, for we know but little of the order of worship here."

"Just that which springs up in your souls is most pleasing to God. I see you have your harps with you. Have you learned to use them?"

"Oh, yes, and I have been practicing some new hymns we sang at our entrance into paradise and at the gate of the city. We used to sing your Psalms of praise on earth, as well as the song of Moses, but when I heard the first strain of music in heaven I concluded we did not know how to sing at all."

"Oh, well," said David, "you will have no trouble in joining in with the music here. Do you not hear the orchestra now? We shall all join them soon."

I had been so entranced at our situation and surroundings and so absorbed in the conversation that I had almost forgotten who or where I was; but turning to Bohemond, I said: "How blessed to be here, and then, just to think, we are with the old prophets of God of whom we have read so much!"

At this Bohemond again fell on his face in adoring praise to God, and poured forth such sweet strains of melodious thanksgiving, that David could not withhold his fingers from the strings of his harp. In a moment more, the whole chariot was sounding with the sweetest music of all the ages, for the sweet singer of Israel had greatly improved himself, he said, since he had been singing the songs of heaven. While we were singing, Bohemond arose and joined, and sang so loud and lovely that all eyes were turned upon him. As I scanned the faces I caught the glimpse of one which I soon recognized as that of Abraham, whom I had met back at the crystal river. I stepped toward him. He knew me and called my name, and shook my hand with a joyous fresh welcome and said: "Let me introduce to you my son Isaac, and Jacob as well, of whom you have often read."

"Oh, is this your son whom you offered on Mount Moriah? And Jacob, thou chosen of God, who wrestled with the angel and prevailed. How blessed to meet you all here! How much like a dream, when we used to read the record of your lives! Oh, my soul is full of glory and praises to God. I am so happy in meeting you here; but you have been here for long ages and I have just come. There are many things I would like to ask you, and I trust in no distant day we may have a long talk. But it does seem good to be here. Just now I remember a Scripture passage which I have read so many times over, but it never had a meaning as it does now. Our Lord once said that "Many should come from the East and the West and should sit down with Abraham, Isaac and Jacob in the kingdom of heaven," (Matthew 8:11), and here it is fulfilled to us. Oh, I do bless God for His great salvation!"

"The music sounds so clear and distinct we must be near the great gathering place for the mighty hosts."

"Indeed, we are," said David. "Cast your eyes abroad and see."

I arose and stood upright in the chariot with one hand on David's shoulder and with the other I held my harp. To my great astonishment, as far as the eye could reach, I saw innumerable hosts gathering and everyone robed in the purest white. The orchestra was still practicing and singing some of the most lovely songs human ears had ever heard. My soul was in a perfect state of rapture and bliss.

The place of the meeting was more like a great amphitheater. The architecture had all been designed by our Lord and is among the things He went to prepare for us. All the seats were beautifully upholstered and the floors carpeted with exquisite taste. Almost without noise or jar everyone found his place. I said to David: "Will our Lord be here among us?"

"No doubt He is here now," answered David, "and will be seated in the center, and all the fresh arrivals will be ushered to seats near Him. This is done to give them a fresh welcome and that all may see the vast hosts of those who are being redeemed and washed by His precious blood; and yet the strangers and newcomers which will be here is only a small portion of those who have so recently entered the portals of paradise, and many of them have entered through the gates into the city."

And true enough, for so it was. All the fresh arrivals were gathered from among the mighty concourse toward the center. Our Lord sat on a kind of elevated throne visible to all the great host. He arose and with most loving words gave us a very kind greeting. A deep sense of awe filled our minds. We knew we were standing in the presence of the Almighty Creator and Gracious Redeemer, and we felt great joy in the kind welcome He gave us. He held up His hands; and the nail prints were also seen in His feet. He did not need a sermon to arouse our feelings of praise. Before time could be given for any further introduction we had all fallen on our faces in adoring praise, for we felt so deeply that all this glory was the purchase of His precious blood, His sufferings and death on the cross of Calvary.

In a few moments we all stood on our feet again and received another gracious welcome by our Lord. His words were most tender and loving and the welcome so sweet and full that at once we all felt perfectly at ease and at home with all the rest of the great company and we all praised God together.

Many hundreds of angels were among us who had carried us from the scenes of our earthly lives into the heavenly domain.

They seemed to rejoice with great joy that we were safely at home in the bosom of God.

Just at this time David arose to his feet and with him many prophets, patriarchs, apostles and ancient servants of God. The song of praise was announced and the whole congregation, having harps of God in their hands, arose. They, or rather we, for we all joined, sang the song of Moses and the song of the Lamb, and the chorus was, "Great and marvelous are Thy works, Lord God Almighty. Just and true are Thy ways, Thou King of Saints. (Revelation 15:3) David's harp played that day as I think it had never played on earth.

Paul and Silas stood side by side and their voices could be distinctly heard above the voices of many. Oh, if only the church on earth could catch the inspiration and life of this heavenly worship, there would be few listless congregations even where there is no preacher at all!

When at last the great congregation had broken up and we were scattering in all directions, we met several ancient men and women who had lived far back in the past ages of the world, with some of whom we had very precious visits.

CHAPTER FIFTEEN

Eighth Visit – Continued
Visit with Ancient Patriarchs

There were many who remained behind long after the great throng had dispersed. Many of these were so filled with the glory of God that they seemed to be holding a kind of after service, which I found was always in order. Like it often is on earth during great revival seasons, the Spirit of God is so infused into the people that a congregation is often loath to leave the scenes of prayer, and while returning to their homes they would be singing the songs of Zion.

I found that the themes of the highest praise in heaven were often those which had been the greatest blessings of earth. The memories of the past and the conscious sense of great deliverances should always bring the soul a deep sense of its indebtedness and gratitude to God. Among those who remained behind were some ancient men joining with the great chorister in many hymns of praise, and singing also many solos of ancient date, of which one could judge by their peculiar wording; referring frequently to events, times, and places of far gone ages; so that we could tell at once that they were ancient men and had lived in a far, remote period of time, although they looked as youthful and full of vigor as any of us who had just entered the city.

To some of these I was especially attracted. Their great earnestness and enthusiasm and peculiar conduct, coupled with such lovely faces and sweet tempers invited us to go and sit among them. So I said to Bohemond, "Let us go and talk with them and find who they are."

They welcomed us to their company. We soon found ourselves sitting in the presence of Job and Methuselah, Abel and Noah, with many of the earliest ancestors of the race. They all seemed full of vigorous life with no marks of decrepit old age like we knew so much in the world. I then quickly thought of the words of the angel to John: "Behold I make all things new," (Revelation 21:5) and sure enough, these were among the earliest of the race of man, made in God's image, on whom this mighty renovating power had come.

We had a long but very pleasant visit with them asking them

63

many questions concerning the early history of man on the earth. Adam and Eve were the first creation of man in the image of God.

We arose to bid them good-bye, when they embraced us with an affectionate kiss and said, "We'll see you again."

Bohemond and myself now went to a quiet place and sat down to talk over the things we had just heard and witnessed for we were most deeply impressed with the words of these ancient men. "Oh," I said, "what is the full and utmost meaning of eternal life? If four thousand years have not made their mark of feebleness, nor dimmed the eye, nor cooled the love and ardor of these men, surely eternity never will."

There were many coming and going, and everyone had such a sweet and holy temper and disposition with such pleasant smiles of loveliness that bespoke eternal satisfaction and contentment. I said to Bohemond: "I have been thinking about a number of my old friends and relatives in the earth who, if they only knew what we know now, they would lead very different lives and seek to be ready for this solid glory."

Bohemond replied: "I almost wish, myself, I could return for just a few days and tell my own people, to whom religion is but little more than an empty profession, the great realities of this heavenly kingdom. I myself never thought it was half so real or could be so grand."

"Well, Bohemond, I would be glad to have you tell me something of your earthly life and surroundings."

"I am descended," said Bohemond, "from a race of kings of Norman blood who reigned for many years at Antioch in Syria. After the close of the dynasty, which occurred about the close of the thirteenth century, our family scattered to different countries, but principally to Bohemia. Our people soon joined in with the Bohemian brethren, many of them becoming earnest followers of Christ. A great persecution arose and many were compelled to hide themselves in dens and caves of the earth. But with the exodus of about a thousand brethren to Poland in the last of the fifteenth century, the honorable sires of our family came.

"By the principles of our faith we were forbidden all kinds of warfare as not comporting with the teaching of our Lord. Because of this and the denial of the doctrine of transsubstantiation, persecution was still heaped upon us. Later on, our particular family moved to Northern Russia where we have been ever since. Many of them have grown wealthy and very prosperous; but I am sad to know that many among them have substituted wealth on earth for treasures in heaven. [*This incident obviously has taken place before Communism took over in Russia in 1917. The Publishers*] If they only knew what was reserved in store for all the redeemed and blood-washed, which we are now enjoying, and were it real to them as it is to us I feel sure they would mightily bestir themselves. Oh, could I send them one warning message from heaven, they would hear me, would they not?"

"Well," I replied, "Abraham was of a different opinion. They have Moses and the prophets; if they would not hear them neither would they hear if one should rise from the dead, so why should we want to return?" We sat long, talking these matters over, but when we aroused ourselves to the situation we found that the great congregation had nearly all gone. But David's chariot still remained standing near the entrance where the hosts had gathered. I said to Bohemond, "Listen a moment. Isn't that lovely music? And the song, oh, how soul-stirring it is." We cast our eyes through the great archway toward the chariot and saw David beckoning us to him. We hastened through the long aisle and when near the chariot, we found it was filled with those holy men of old. David now said: "We saw you were quite alone and thought you would like to go with us to a great praise service for the children soon to be held near the Judean gate." We gladly accepted their offer, saying, "We were on our way to the throne, but will be glad to go with you for we are but little acquainted with the city." Paul spoke lovingly, and yet laughingly, and said: "Well, dear brethren, I have been here for more than eighteen hundred years and yet I know but little of the city, although I have been to many sections of it again and again. Our inheritance is exceeding great." Don't hurry — eternity is before you. The vast plains of paradise," said Paul, "and all the riches of the eternal city are yours forever."

"Now," said David, "step up and take a seat beside Paul and myself. Those brethren in the rear of the chariot would be glad to speak to you." The four men arose, and we were introduced to Elias and Daniel, whom everyone knows, and who are famous in heaven on account of their devotion and service to

God in the earth, and a man by the name of Artorious, of whom I had never heard before. (David said he was from Southern Mesopotamia and a descendant from Shem and one of Abraham's soldiers in the battle at Hobah in the King's Dale, and John, the beloved disciple, whose name is a household word in all the world.

"Well, brethren," I said, "is it true that we are here with those who have lived so long ago? The idea of immortality and a future life, which we cherished so dearly in the world has proven more than a dream. Oh, how good it is to be here! There are so many things I want to ask you concerning a far by-gone age, but my soul is too full of glory and praises to God now, I cannot restrain my feelings." David said: "You need not try. We will all join you in praises to God." Silas arose from the front of the chariot and came and stood by David's side while they sang a most lovely hymn. Bohemond and I fell on our faces in the chariot and worshipped God, blessed Giver of all this good."

"Now," said Seneca, "I must leave these holy men and the chariot till I see you again," and so saying he bade me good night.

CHAPTER SIXTEEN

Ninth Visit
Enroute for the Children's Meeting

I was very anxious for Seneca's return for he had left the chariot filled with men enroute for the children's polytechnic and the remainder of his narrative I was exceedingly anxious to hear.

A gentle rap at the door, it opened, and my silken bearded friend stepped in. "I am glad to see you, Mr. Sodi, I have always welcomed you, but never more than tonight. I have everything ready for your message."

"You shall write it, my son," he said, and he began:

David led in the singing of the hymn. The chariot was moving slowly along. When we finished David said to his charioteer: "You may drive past the children's polytechnic, and let our brethren so lately come see what our Lord has prepared for the little ones of His kingdom." So, turning to the right, he guided the chariot, not rapidly, for we had many things to talk about on the way.

The avenue was broad and lovely. We passed many gushing fountains and groves of the trees of life. These were not for shade as no burning sun smites either the city or the blessed paradise.

On the way I said to Paul, who sat by my side: "It does seem so good to be here with you, it seems indeed too good to be true. Fancy painted many fair pictures while we were in the world which were made to glow on the canvas of our imagination in reference to the future, but none ever equalled the reality."

"No," said Paul, "it was impossible for man to conceive of the glory while in the flesh. The Lord once gave me just a glimpse into paradise while yet in the world. The glory was beyond my power to describe."

I replied to Paul: "I have often wondered how it occurred, for we have a brief account in the divine word on earth which you left concerning it." (II Corinthians 12:2)

"Well," said he, "while at Lystra in Lyconia I was stoned and dragged out of the city for dead, but God raised me up, and

I, with the brethren, went back to the city. (Acts 14:19) But that night I could not sleep, being restless and burdened with the word of the Lord. I arose and, all alone, went out of the city to pray. I ascended the side of old Karadogh, an extinct volcano. I seemed to be greatly helped, for an angel constantly held my hand. When some little distance up the mountain, one of the chariots of God, with a driver of light, appeared at my side. I was so enraptured by the presence and glory of God and both overawed and overcome by the royal chariot and driver that I hardly could tell whether I had died or was in a trance; but I soon found myself lying prostrate in the chariot and mounting far above the old mountain. We arose above the pillars of the skies. I soon heard the strains of music from the third heaven in the plains of paradise. They were singing some new songs, which as a mortal man, I had not power to repeat. I opened my eyes just for a moment, glanced at the crystal river and heard a loud voice proclaiming the mystery of the trees upon its banks. It was the closing words of a sermon uttered by Moses to a vast company of Jews, as I was told by the driver afterwards, giving them light upon these that they could not know while under the law and subject to an inferior experience, for you have already found that we have preaching here in heaven as we used to have on earth.

"Only an instant we remained and the chariot darted with the speed of sound toward the earth. In a few moments the old town of Lystra, lying at the foot of the mountain, with its streets and domes, shore out with their best appearance under the light of the full moon beaming upon them; but the people were fast asleep. I stepped from the chariot as the driver, with a pleasant wave of his hand, said, good-bye, and in an instant it was gone. On the top of Karadogh I continued my prayer and praise to God until near the break of day. I never could really tell while in my flesh whether I was loosened for the time being from my body or whether bodily I was taken to glory. Ever after this I had a longing to go back and forever remain; to depart and be with Christ. The words of the sermon and the strains of music could never be forgotten, but were an element of strength in my life during the many afflictions God permitted to come upon me."

"I remember the words in your Epistle," I replied: "For me to live is Christ and to die is gain. For I am in a strait betwixt two having a desire to depart and be with Christ which is far better." (Philippians 1:21)

"Indeed," said Paul, "and had I known all the bliss and glory of the celestial kingdom, as it is, I could not have been contented. I was greatly favored of God, and through so many revelations of His will and manifestations of His power I was in great danger of being unduly exalted; but God always knows how to deal with us for our greatest good. A man of most bitter wrath was turned against me, indeed he was a thorn in the flesh to me. He was the messenger of Satan; but God's grace then, as at all times, was entirely sufficient for me, and I always found that all things work together for good to them who love God."

"Oh, thank you much for your words. It seems as if God directed you to give me this little bit of your experience. I have often wondered what the thorn was to which you alluded in the Epistle."

"Yes," said Paul, "but this messenger of Satan, as well as the prisons, scourges, beatings, betrayals by false brethren, and sufferings of earth, only worked for my good. I am so blessedly free from them all now. The contrast is so great it gives me an eternal appreciation of the blessedness of this kingdom."

"I see," said David, "we are coming near the children's spiritual Polytechnic. Can you hear them singing?" "Oh, most distinctly," and yet, the place was still out of sight. The streets were thronged with the little ones, usually in company with the angels or faithful mothers or those having care over them. They all seemed so joyous and their laugh of hilarity and joyful conversation bespoke perfect contentment and satisfaction, and yet we knew that much the larger number had left their parents in the earth; but there is no grief nor sorrow in heaven. If all mothers in earth could only see their children whom they have lost, as they really are, they would weep no more, but make every provision needed to soon follow them to those mansions of light!"

Many older people were among them. Some were parents conducting their children. Some small infants were carried by the angels, or precious women had them pressed close to their bosoms, for their infant feet had never learned to walk.

At last our chariot halted just near the great entrance, where it seemed countless throngs were pouring in, and of all this great host none had been within the compass of the heavenly domain but a short time. Children soon grow to maturity in heaven. Your little babe, dear mother of earth, which left you many years ago, is now with its harp of gold singing and praising God in all the maturity of its manhood or womanhood.

We now stepped out and followed the great throng whither they went.

CHAPTER SEVENTEEN

Ninth Visit – Continued
The Children's Great Cathedral

The place was most beautiful indeed. The decorations were beyond description, for everyone seemed to take an interest in the children and had brought flowers celestial, worked into bouquets and wreaths of artistic beauty, with blooming shrubbery of an unfading character and of many kinds. I thought of the Scripture, "Strength and beauty are in His sanctuary." "Beautiful and grand indeed!" I whispered. The decorations overhead, the carpets underfoot, the upholstery and cushions were of the finest fabric, with tiny seats also of celestial velvet, for the little ones. A thousand golden chains sparkling with diamonds, and gems of rarest beauty were arranged for the leaders in the service. A large and beautifully arranged platform was in the center on which several thousand could sit or stand, elevated so that all could easily be seen and heard. This was for the leaders in the great public services.

Great multitudes of children were rapidly filing in, and gathering towards this great center. They had escorts guiding them to their respective places. They, like all the inhabitants of heaven, were clothed in shining garments of the purest white. They had all entered the portals of the heavenly domain at some point of paradise, for it will be remembered that all souls enter paradise first of all, and as they are prepared for the fuller enjoyment of the King and His glory, they pass on toward the throne where God Himself is seen and enjoyed in all His glory and majesty.

All these children had been for a longer or shorter period in the preparatory departments of paradise; but they had now entered through the gates with greatly extended privileges.

As I glanced over the countless multitude of little ones, I was most forcibly reminded of the words of our Lord: "Suffer the children to come unto me, and forbid them not, for of such is the kingdom of heaven. (Mark 10:14) I thought again that no longer was the warning needed that "Whosoever shall offend one of these little ones which believe in me, it were better for him that a millstone were hanged about his neck and that he were drowned in the depths of the sea." (Mark 9:42) "No," I thought, thank God, no more experiences of being cuffed about as many had been on earth. No more little heartaches and sobs. No more being falsely accused and blamed by irritated older ones!"

I thought as I looked over this wonderful gathering that every child had a history of its own. I thought of little Mary and her sad story of whom we used to sing on earth. A mother who was preparing some flour for baking into cakes left it for a few minutes when little Mary, with childish curiosity to see what it was, took hold of the dish which fell to the floor spilling the contents. The mother struck the child a severe blow, saying, with anger, that she was always in the way. A fortnight afterward little Mary's sickness had increased to her death. On her death bed while delirious she asked her mother if there would be any room for her among the angels. "I was always in your way, mother, you had no room for me at times in your heart. And shall I be in the angels' way?" The broken-hearted mother then felt no sacrifice too great, could she have saved the child.

When the dewy light was fading
And the sky in beauty smiled,
Came this whisper, like an echo,
From a pale and dying child:

"Mother, in that golden region
With its pearly gates so fair,
Up among the happy angels,
Is there room for Mary there?

"Mother, raise me just a moment;
You'll forgive me when I say
You were angry when you told me
I was always in your way.

"You were sorry in a moment,
I could read it on your brow,
But you'll not recall it, mother;
You must never mind it now.

"When my baby sister calls me
And you hear my voice no more;
When she plays among the roses
By our little cottage door;

"Never chide her when you're angry.
Do it kindly and in love:
That you both may dwell with Mary,
In the sunny land above."

Then she plumed her snowy pinions
Till she folded them to rest.
Mid the welcome song of rapture
On the loving Saviour's breast.

In the bright and golden regions,
With its pearly gates so fair,
She is singing with the angels.
Yes, there's room for Mary there.

I wondered and said to myself, "Is she among these countless throngs I see?" Everyone seemed to be so contented and happy and without that feeling of loneliness and fear which is so natural to all children on earth when absent from parents or home. They seemed to be so rational and appreciative of their situation. Some of them had died when tiny infants and had known nothing of the earth, so they seemed to be somewhat amused at the story of their former life and beginning in the world. Oh, this wonderful scene: the grandest I have ever witnessed either on earth or in heaven," I said to Bohemond. "My whole soul is in raptures of delight. We could hear the voices of thousands who were praising God, with loud, yet most sweet words, and with their harps of gold. The great amphitheater was simply ringing with the melodies of heaven. David's chariot stood still on the street; but he with the remainder of our company had gone on toward the great central gathering, for our Lord Himself was seated on the platform and blessing the multitude as they came past. His blessing was filled with such enlightening grace that the children bounded off with such intelligent praise that one might think they had been here for many years.

Just at this moment I was much gladdened to see dear mother coming toward me. I had parted from her at my first introduction to Moses when she went outside the gate to assist a group of these little ones.

"Oh, mother," I shouted, "I am so glad to meet you again. Have you been with these children ever since you left me when we were talking with Moses, for you went to take charge of a group of children singing their songs just outside the gate?"

"Yes, indeed, and they are now among this mighty concourse praising God and for the first time they look upon their Saviour's face and receive His gracious welcome."

CHAPTER EIGHTEEN

Ninth Visit — Continued
The Praise Service

"I should like to know who this is with you, mother, who seems to bear the family likeness." I noticed an anxious smile upon the face of a beautiful young woman who stood beside her.

"Well," said my mother, "I have been waiting to see if you would recognize her, for you once knew her as a little infant."

"Oh, mother, I want to know if this is my own darling child who left us when only three months from her birth."

"Indeed," replied mother, "this is your child and I have watched over her ever since she came into paradise."

From that moment she fell upon my neck with deep and sweet praises to God. We could not weep, for there are no tears in heaven, but our rejoicing was more precious than anything I had ever known on earth. "Well," I said, "dear child, I only knew you as a little infant, but now you have grown to womanhood. We wept much when you died, for our home was deserted and stripped of all the light and joy which you brought into it. Your mother and I were not active Christians then, but for many days and nights we could hear your voice with a plaintive cry beckoning us to this city of light."

"Oh," said Mary, for that was her name, "it was the angel who carried me to paradise, for he went back to speak to you for your cheer and comfort, so he told me later on."

"Well, my dear child, I am so glad to see you once again after more than forty years have passed, now grown to your maturity. How graceful you look! You must have been well cared for."

"Cared for! No soul lacks attention in heaven. This your mother has been my mother since my tiny life in paradise began. But I have often met my real mother, for she was here long before you came. Have you not met her yet?"

"No, dear child, but I know I will soon. I have asked after her quite often, but I find she is detained in some distant place in paradise assisting a group of young people lately come, but who were not prepared for the glory of the city, and she cannot leave them just now."

"Yes," said Mary, "I know quite well where she is and have been to see her often."

"Among many others whose bodies were buried beside your own we lost your little grave, but we knew you were not lost. The meeting which we had in prospect seemed so like a dream, but, oh, how real it is! Your mother no doubt has told you all about our family which you never knew, but when we have an opportunity we will talk it all over."

"Oh, indeed, I will be delighted to hear you tell me all about each one of them – no, I mean, each one of us."

"Well, dear mother, I am glad you have brought my child to me. But will you tell me something about the law of growth and development in heaven from that of a tiny infant to the maturity and development which I see before me?"

"Well, you know that the trees of life have twelve kinds of fruit, adapted to all the needs of the human soul. There is no lack of opportunity, for the means of knowledge and instruction are abundantly offered here, according to the growing demands of each soul. Yet the growth and development of each depends much upon its own efforts. There are but few idle people in heaven and yet traits of character developed on earth during the formative period of life continue with us here unless they are changed or overcome during the probationary state. Everyone has his identity and peculiar characteristics developed during his life. If an individual was careless and indolent in his earthly life, the same tendencies continue with him here. There is, however, no such thing as a stubborn or obstinate spirit among all these children, nor in all heaven. Every will bows in sweet harmony with God; but some make more rapid advancement than others, which depends upon their own exertions and energy. As they apply themselves to all the means of instruction and partake wisely of the fruit of the trees, they move along the lines of heavenly development. A simlar law prevails here as on earth. Natural law indeed is extended into the spiritual realm. Our souls never cease to grow and develop intellectually and expand their grasp of eternal realities. There is a grand perfection in heaven which admits of an eternal progress toward the fulness of our great Father in whose image we all are. But as on earth, so in the kingdom of heaven, much of our duty and labor of love is for each other, and ever will be."

I then said to my mother: "Persons who have been separated

but a short time will see and know each other much as they saw them when they parted in the world."

"Quite the same," she said, "only the difference between the earthly and the heavenly state. But in the case of parents whose little ones were taken in infancy and the parents remained in the world for many years, they shall not meet them as infants, but like yours, developed toward maturity."

"Oh, yes, I see, it would be a great calamity if they should remain tiny infants or were untaught little children."

"Now, cast your eyes over this great company," said mother, "You see multitudes of classes formed and the angels, elders, and more experienced ones are teaching them the knowledge of heaven and new hymns of praise, and soon we will all join in some choruses and if you have never heard music, you will hear it now, when all these children are praising God together, for most of them have learned to use their harps."

Mary, who had been standing nearby listening to our conversation, came up close and said: "I am so glad, dear father, to see you here. How long since you have come?"

"Only a short time," I replied.

"I hope soon to hear all about our family since mother left you and even before, for you may tell me some things she has not. I do not know why I was taken from you so early; but our good Father knows best and all He does is best and just at the right time. I remember being a little infant in your arms and on mother's breast, but I haven't much recollection of the world, but I am told it is much inferior to this land of light and joy."

Her memory was doing its work. She took me by the hand and fell upon my neck once more and began to praise God in such sweet tones that it seemed for the time that all the events for nearly forty years were annihilated and we stood as father and infant.

Just at this moment my companions of the chariot, who had gone on toward the center of the great hall, beckoned to me. We all went toward them and at a given signal the mighty concourse fell upon their faces in adoring praise to Him who was in the midst and was fairer than the sons of men. Many of these children looked upon His blessed face for the first time. Such a welcome He gave them, which showed His great love for the little ones.

The harps were all tuned to the voice of the singer, and

as we now arose, all stood, and many with outstretched hands toward Him with one great voice made the arches and domes of heaven to resound with melodious infant praises. How forcibly I again remembered the words, "Suffer the little children to come unto me for of such is the kingdom of heaven." (Mark 10:14)

These meetings I found were frequently for the children in which they were taught the worship of God and instructed concerning the sad fact of sin, and that without the great atoning sacrifice of their Lord, none of them could ever have entered the blessed portals of this heavenly domain. They were taught about His sufferings and death for them; the sin and awful fall of our first parents in Eden, and how judgment came upon all to condemnation, and that an eternal night of hell would have been theirs if their Lord had not suffered for them. I noticed their intense interest in the story of the cross and their deep appreciation of what the Lord had done for them. The prints of the nails yet in His hands and feet were an object lesson to them indeed.

The time came at last for dismissal. The great concourse arose, and the doxology began:

> Praise God, Great Author of all love,
> Praise Him all creatures here above,
> Praise Him below, a mighty host:
> Praise Father, Son, and Holy Ghost.

[*In heaven the wording of doxology is changed to fit the place where it is sung.*]

As we sang the doxology, it seemed that earth and heaven had united. The veil between seemed very thin. In fact, we knew we were all one great family and that very soon all of earth's redeemed would be forever together. The benediction was pronounced by our Lord Himself, with such blessed words of heavenly love, it seemed like He might almost be back upon earth blessing the little children.

We were soon scattering in all directions, but the children's joyous songs and faces beaming with such expression of contentment, as they were passing through the great archway, constantly attracted my attention.

I said, "What perfect satisfaction, so complete is their joy!

They have all the association anyone could wish. No ones cares for association not found here. There is no danger, nor any feeling of fear. There is no one in all the wide domain of this heavenly kingdom with any evil intent or desire, but perfect confidence and trust in every soul."

David who came near me just then with his harp strings trembling with an air of peculiar sweetness and who seemed to be enjoying the grand procession as well, stopped nearby. I said to him: "Do you find any homesick children wanting to go back to their old homes in the earth?"

"Not one," he replied. "If parents could only see and know this glory into which their children have entered they would not mourn over their departure from the earth so bitterly."

I said to David: "I remember just now your word concerning your own child when it had died: your grief had been most intolerable during its sickness, but when it was dead, you said, "I shall go to him, but he shall not return to me." (II Samuel 12:23)

"Yes," said David, "and I have been with him nearly three thousand years in this glory. Twenty years after his death I followed him and found he had grown to mature years and had been a thousand times in similar places as this and much instructed in the ways of the eternal city."

"Now," said Seneca, "I must leave you rest. The hour is late and you are tired." "But, " I replied to him, "are you not tired also?" "No, I never tire any more, nor ever feel weary; but I long to get back to my Father's house. Just as soon as my task to the world is done through you, I shall speed with all haste to my treasures above. Be of good cheer, my son. A reward is in waiting for you." So saying he bade me good night and vanished from my sight.

CHAPTER NINETEEN

Tenth Visit
Seneca Sodi, with Mother and Daughter, Returns to Paradise in David's Chariot
An Earthly Sermon Repeated in Heaven

"You are on good time tonight, Seneca, and I am rested and ready for my evening's task."

"I am glad, " said Mr. Sodi, *"to see you in good humor and in such fine spirits. May the Almighty Father bless you tonight as I give you my message:*

As we were leaving the children's great convocation, David came and asked if we would like to take a hasty trip into paradise. As his chariot was now going, we gladly accepted the invitation, and in a short time mother, myself and daughter stepped out of the chariot a thousand leagues from the gate of Manasseh. This was a new but most beautiful place in paradise to us. David said: "Enjoy yourselves as you like. I will call for you later," and his chariot moved on. In the distance I saw another chariot slackening its speed. Four souls clothed in the garments of heaven were seated within. To one of them I was particularly drawn. He was clothed in a white gown only. The moment he found he was within the gates of paradise and opening his eyes upon the glory before him he fell prostrate upon his face with the deepest emotion, both of praise and regrets over the past. He was greatly bewildered over the glory of which he felt so unworthy. He tried to praise God but could not look up for shame, he was so nearly naked. One of the saints who seemed to understand his situation addressed him and said: "You are saved. Think not of your past. What God has forgiven He remembers no more."

"Yes," said the man, but I am so unworthy. The angels assured me that the gate would be open for me. Only a few hours ago I was a lost sinner and far from God. I have come direct from the jaws of eternal death. Oh, tell me, am I in heaven? The sermon I cannot forget. Oh, how God blessed the preacher! His words went to my heart. I was grieving over my sins and crying. I was praying. Oh, how Jesus revealed Himself to me, and gave me rest! I was on my dying bed. A meeting appointed and the house was crowded, only last night. Oh, tell me, I pray you, am I in heaven?"

"You are safe," the saint replied, "safe at home. Can you repeat any of the sermon to us?"

"Indeed I can; every word of it. Hosea 10:12. Is it time to seek the Lord? At 5 a.m. when the first gleams of the morning appear, you ask, 'Is it time to seek the Lord?' A voice from heaven whispers, 'They that seek me early shall find me.' At 7 a.m. again you ask, 'Is it now time to seek the Lord?' A voice from the throne replies: 'Remember now thy Creator in the days of thy youth.' Oh, what a beautiful light is circling round the brow and becoming a center of joy within the character of that child of God who has early learned to lisp the name of Jesus! Again at 9 a.m. the bell calls and you ask, 'Is it time to seek the Lord?' Conscience trembles and says, 'I have passed many an open door of grace already and the sins of my youth are multiplied.' As you listen to the voice you hear it saying, 'Now is the accepted time: now is the day of salvation.' High noon has now come to many a soul here. The most important period of life has already past or is now upon you. The golden opportunities of childhood and youth will return to you no more. Yet you say with an indifferent air, 'Is it time for me to seek the Lord?' Satan now begins to whisper, 'Your heart is hard, you cannot easily repent with all your cares upon you.'

"Turn your eyes upward and listen," the preacher said, "as you say, 'what must I do to be saved?' Everything within you has been saying, 'Repent, repent.' Now the echo comes back from heaven as though sounded with the trump of God: "Repent ye and believe the gospel. Come unto me and I will give you rest. In the day that ye seek me with all the heart I will be found of you.'

"Consider your situation as it is in God's sight. Think you of the littleness of time that is left you for so great a preparation. Think you of your accountability to God. You will soon stand before Him, and render an impartial account of your stewardship. Think you of your reply to Him who sitteth upon the throne when He shall say, 'Friend, how comest thou in hither not having on a wedding garment?' (Matthew 22:12) Oh, think you of your feelings when you will look this way and that, to find yourself so confounded that you are speechless, as you call back the days when showers of grace from heaven fell so often upon you and your heart yielded no fruit of righteousness in return. Think of the barren fig tree that stood so many years in the vineyard, having been digged about and watered so long without any fruit; that when mercy shall cry, 'cut it down,' anticipate your sorrow and think what your feelings will be.

"Think deeply of the weeds which have been growing in your heart so long and scattering their seed in other soil around you. Think of the ripening harvest from your sowing, and that "whatsoever a man soweth that shall he also reap.' Think of the rich man in torment, remembering good only to lighten his sorrow, knowing it might have been otherwise with his soul, but now being tormented he could see 'Lazarus afar off in Abraham's bosom.'

"As these considerations are before you, haste with all speed to Him who alone is able to save you. Oh, do not live longer as if there were neither a bed of death nor a bar of judgment. Be wise; look your danger in the face. Anticipate the day when you shall behold a God in judgment and a world in flames; and flee to your God from the wrath to come." With this the man bowed his head again and with sobs of emotion mingled with joy and grief, he arose and said: "Oh, thank God, I remember it all and was earnestly praying when the chariot called for me. Oh, I did and do hate every sin of the past. I do love God. I am His forever. Hallelujah to Jesus!"

Quite a group had gathered to hear this sermon. When he had finished we all united in one great shout of praise to God. "Oh, yes," he said, "I am in heaven! Thank God for His everlasting mercy. I am out of hell. I am in heaven."

When he had finished his sermon my mother and daughter went to him and said: "Good brother, we rejoice with you that you are in heaven. You see your folly in not having made better preparation for this land of light and love, but be faithful to every opportunity for your advancement. Your escorts will conduct you into the ways and laws of this heavenly kingdom. I also gave him words of cheer, and he began to praise God again and said, "I do bless God for that preacher. His words were surely sent by the Holy Spirit. They went like an arrow to my soul."

At this an elder came and said to him: "Be of good cheer, my brother, the angels have brought you safely to this paradise and far toward the interior from the gate of entrance. Many of the ancient saints spend much time about the threshold of paradise and assist all who enter. But a large number of them have just been up to some great praise services within the city and have not yet returned, and the angel has brought you here. Pay good heed to all your opportunities, for much is before you."

"Oh," he cried out, "only let me know what I must do to be in harmony with this holy place. Oh, heaven, thou art mine! Am I at all purified from my sin? Oh, am I acceptable to God, will He welcome me?"

"Surely," said the elder, "when you are prepared for the light and glory of the city, you will be brought to its gates and ushered in with the welcome of your Lord. If you tarry among these trees, do not be restless nor neglectful. Almost the entire catalogue of the Christian graces must be learned by you. Partake freely of the twelve kinds of fruit on the trees; they will impart light, life and grace to your soul. Press the leaves to your nostrils and bind them to your heart and no taint of evil will abide in you."

At this we saw David's chariot coming in the distance.

CHAPTER TWENTY

Tenth Visit – Continued
Martyred Saints in Heaven
An Excursion to the Hills

David's chariot was now here. With him were a number of new arrivals but who were full fledged saints of earth. With exultant praises they were glorifying God. Their faces beaming with the light of heaven. David called to us, saying: "I'll see you again later. Go where you will. I must take these dear brethren far up the river toward the gate of Manasseh, where they will spend some time among the trees which you can see in the far distance yonder." As the chariot moved off, David's harpstrings were trembling to the words of the twenty-fourth Psalm, in which all had joined.

My mother now said: "Yonder comes four beautiful spirits whom I want you to meet. They are the most joyful souls I have met in a long time. I have often met them in the city and know them quite well."

As they came nearer I asked her who they were.

"They were of the martyred saints," she replied. "They were all burnt at the stake, for their testimony for our Lord."

"Oh, mother, I shall be so glad to meet them."

"And I too," said Mary.

By this time they were very near us. A wonderful halo of glory was about them.

"Good morning," said mother, for everyone says good morning in heaven for a long time after they have entered paradise or even the city gates, for it seems as though morning had only come, one feels so refreshed, happy and light-hearted. They returned the greeting with a lovely bow and handshake. We were soon introduced and a lively conversation following and indeed it was a joyful interview. Their holy, heavenly laugh and joyful expressions filled my soul with rapture of praise.

"My mother has just told me that you are of those who once suffered martyrdom for Christ's sake."

"Yes, said one of them, "we remember those days of awful persecution as though it were but yesterday. But many hundreds of years have passed since then and we are amply repaid for it here. They tried hard to induce us to recant; but no,

84

our Lord's words were too close to our hearts for that. He had said: "Fear not them which kill the body but are not able to kill the soul, but rather fear him which is able to destroy both soul and body in hell." (Matthew 10:28) Our sufferings were intense; but it was soon over and we were immediately ushered into this glory. As we leaped from the body we shouted victory over fire and enemies.

As they uttered these words I thought of the Scripture where John, the beloved disciple, said: "I saw under the altar the souls of them that were slain for the word of God and for the testimony which they held. And they cried with a loud voice, saying:

'How long, O Lord, holy and true, dost thou not judge and avenge our blood on them that dwell on the earth?' And white robes were given to every one of them, and it was said unto them that they should rest yet for a little season until their fellow servants also and their brethren should be killed as they were." (Revelation 6:10,11)

"Indeed," said they all, "and our rest has been most sweet among these bowers of paradise and the glories of the eternal city." "It is here," said one of them, "as it used to be on earth when the old soldiers of war times would have their reunions and jollifications, and talk over the memories of their awful struggles. We are just now enroute for a great reunion of the martyrs and confessors of our Lord during the dark ages of bitter persecution on earth. In a little while you will see many chariots bringing their thousands to what we call here, "Our excursion to the hills." We would be pleased to have you go along with us."

Mary quickly spoke up and said: "Yes, let us go."

We quickly dropped in with them and walked to the station just near. While waiting for a chariot I said to mother and Mary: "I am so glad of this meeting. I have heard so much of the days of awful persecution and of the thousands who were killed by fire and sword. Nero's persecution at Rome was an awful time when he burnt so many of the saints. Smearing their nude bodies with pitch and making midnight torches of them, and their agonizing cries were the music for his chariot races."

"It was terrible," said mother, "but they are all here now with the glory of God upon them. No doubt we will meet many of them soon."

85

"Look," said Mary, "do you see the chariots coming?"

"Oh, yes, in the distance," I replied. "Is their route past this station?"

"I think so," said one of the saints, and with that he waved the flowing ends of his mantle and a charioteer seeing him turned his chariot toward us. As it came near, I noticed there were a number of coaches attached somewhat like our railroad train coaches on earth. I did not yet know the propelling power of the chariots, but something akin to the electrical currents of earth, mightily operated these wonderful fliers of heaven. But of this matter I will speak to you again later, if you wish.

As the chariot slowed its speed and drew near us, we all stepped aboard and were greeted within, by hundreds of the most joyous people I have met in heaven. The chariot moved on with wonderful rapidity toward the pleasure parks and hillsides of paradise. When, at last, it slowed up amid a mighty host gathering from all parts of the city, of those who had been beheaded and martyred for Christ's sake. Many of them had suffered untold anguish and tortures in prisons, at racks and inquisitions, torn of wild beasts in the arena of amphitheaters for the amusement of wicked men. We saw many of those alluded to in the blessed book which now lies on your table; where it speaks of Gideon and Barak and Samson and Jephthah and David and Samuel and the prophets and others which had trials of cruel mockings and scourgings, or bonds and imprisonments. We saw those who had been stoned, sawn asunder, were tempted, were slain with the sword, who had wandered about in sheepskins and goatskins, being destitute, afflicted, tormented: Of whom the world was not worthy. They had wandered in deserts and in mountains and dens and caves of the earth.

Among them we saw James whom Herod killed with the sword; and Stephen whom they stoned; in fact, nearly all the apostles were there. We saw also Latimer and Thomas Hawks and a hundred beside who had suffered in England as martyrs under the reign of her who was called "Bloody Mary." But they with the thousands of others who had sealed their testimony with their own blood, were the most joyful of all men whom I had met in all the heavenly domain. During the course of the exercises of the occasion and the joyful and exultant praises from this great army of saints over whom neither fire, sword, nor prison could avail to turn them aside from the holy confession of Jesus, I kept thinking of that Scripture where in the Revelation of St. John he says: "I saw the souls of them who were beheaded for the witness of Jesus and for the word of God, and which had not worshipped the beast neither his image, neither had received his mark upon their foreheads, nor in their hands; and they lived and reigned with Christ a thousand years." (Revelation 20:4)

Just at this time Paul came to us and seeing I was but a newcomer to this great feast, said to me: "Were you a martyr for Jesus?" I said, "No, but I truly love Him and hope I am not intruding."

"Oh, no," he replied, "you are indeed welcome."

I was then emboldened to ask him to explain that Scripture just quoted.

"Certainly," said he, "all this great host who have suffered for Christ on earth shall also likewise reign with Him on earth. The millennial sabbath is almost to dawn, when for a thousand years these will be greatly honored among the hosts of heaven when the Lord shall return to earth with all His saints. They shall reign with Him. This honor have all the martyred saints, for they who suffer with Him shall also reign with Him."

When the great assembly had closed its business session (for there is much business carried on in heaven of which the business in the earth is but child's play in comparison), then followed the praise service which for enthusiasm and spiritual activity would put to blush most of our active service in the church on earth. The harps and stringed instruments of heaven, in the hands of these trained choristers, simply made the arches and domes of heaven ring. Souls developed under such trials of suffering as these had passed through, who make up this mighty convocation, brought forth the sweetest and loveliest melodies, until I was simply bewildered in the consideration of the capacity and developement of a human soul in heaven.

Following this was a heavenly picnic, which for joy and gladness and demonstration of victories and praise, nothing in earth will compare to it. Fruits of many kinds with the various spices and viands of the eternal world were prepared for the lunch. Angels were busy at this service. It was difficult for me to learn of the multitudes of good things prepared for these saints, there was such an abundance. After all had eaten, then the thousands began their rambles through the valleys and among the hills and mountains of paradise. Great gorges with stupendous cataracts and magnificent scenery and pleasant places of rest and enjoyment abounding everywhere. Perpetual blooming flowers with groves of trees and carpets of grass with such endless varieties bring their constant rewards to those who rest from their labors, with an eternal satisfaction in this blest paradise above.

CHAPTER TWENTY-ONE

Tenth Visit – Continued
No Race Prejudice in Heaven

At the close of the great convocation, mother came to me and said: "Son, have you noticed there is no race prejudice in heaven?"

"No distinctions of the races, mother?"

Yes, there are distinctions, but no prejudice because of race. It makes no difference here as to the kind of body we had on earth. All souls have a spotless whiteness here and their robes, the same. Whatever the physical condition may have been on earth, we are all one family here. Children of one Father. Do you notice that group of singers yonder?"

"I do, mother."

"They were all colored people of America," she said "some of them suffered much, as slaves, by their old masters. Let us go and speak to them a moment."

We did so, when to my great surprise I quickly recognized one of them. We stood face to face, but for a moment I hesitated, and then said: "In the name of paradise, is this you, Rastus?"

"Oh," he said, "It's me; but who be you?"

I said, "Look again."

He did so and began to smile. "I do know you, Mr. Sodi, you preached to us colored folks once on board the vessel on de North Sea," and with that he gave me his hand.

I knew him in my earlier years having business with his old master in the South. He was very black and very ignorant, but his face now shone with the brightness of heaven itself, and his garments were perfect whiteness.

"Well, I am glad to meet you," he said.

"Indeed, it is mutual," I replied; "but you are so changed. Are there no black faces in heaven?" I inquired.

"Oh," he said, "we are all white here and in de perfect image of de Lord."

I asked what his old master thought of the great exaltation into which he had come.

"My master," said he, "I fear is not here. I have never seen him since I escaped him and went to Northern Russia on de vessel of which you know. De floggin' had been a hard one and I determined he'd never give me anoder one. So after de vessel was full of de cotton bales I hid underneath 'em till she was well out at sea, when I made myself known because of hunger and thirst. They made many threats to throw me over into the sea, like to Jonah; but my life was spared and I escaped to Russia. Neither have I seen him in dis heavenly world. I have passed to and fro among these countless hosts of de redeemed and have been to very many sections of de city, but I have not met him. I fear he is not here. He used to attend de services of his church and made a good profession on de Sunday, but during de week he was ungodly and rough to his children and still worse to us his slaves. I have been made to feel so deeply de folly of servin' de Lord one day in de seven and de devil de nex' six. Thousands are lost tryin' to serve two masters and peerin' to be good on de Sunday and let de devil rule 'em de rest of de week. Oh, I was so poor in de world; my cabin had no window, nor did we have a rag of a carpet on de floor, nor a picture on de wall, neither did we have a flower in de yard nor did we have a yard, for the cotton growed to de door.

"But oh, I have everything here; everything I kin see is mine. And all beside and still it belongs to all dese udder people just as much as me. I goes just where I like, up and down de streets, through de long avenues, out through de gates of de city in de blessed chariots of God, to de infinite regions of dis paradise; and de Lord Jesus has given me entire liberty and says, "Go jis whar you will, and eat of every tree you like. Clime de mountains and go into de valley and along de rivers and bathe your soul in de sunshine of de Lamb, who is de light of all de heavenly city and dis paradise."

"Well, Rastus," I said to him, "I am very glad to meet you here and witness how God has lifted you up from the dust and the dung hill and made you a prince among His saints."

"Indeed, I am gladder dan you kin be. I am de object of His grace and you de witness. But when did you come to de city?"

"This," I replied, "is my first visit to paradise after having been in the city only a short time. I have only just begun to see my inheritance."

"Well," said he, "you will never git tired lookin' into de great mysteries of de eternal city. Nor will your heart ever shrivel again under de cold blasts of de world of sin; but it will

90

swell wid de highest emotions of praise. Do you see dis harp (which he loosened from his girdle and began to test the strings)? I keep it tuned up all de time ready for de praise of de Lord Jesus. Oh, if I only could meet my ole master of de earth a comin' along the street some day; den de angels would have to minister de first rebuke in heaven, and say, "Not quite so loud wid de music over in dat corner; for you disturb de children's meetin' on the fourth avenue." But I fear I shall never meet him, for God says, dar shall in no wise enter into de city anything dat defileth, neither whatsoever worketh abomination or maketh a lie; but dey which are written in de Lamb's book of life. He used to defile de women of de plantation and lead others to do the same, and do other immoral abominations; dar was no end to 'em, and den de matter was, he would cover it up and seem to be a saint on de Sunday. Oh, I fear his hopeless cries will never reach to de throne. And yet some day one of de angels may come to me sayin' I have good news for you; your old master is at last earnestly prayin' and washin' hisself wid his tears and de soap of de word. Den dis ole harp would begin on de highest key, until de angel would have to say, 'Rastus, you had better drop back to de key of F, for he's a leper from de sole of his foot to de crown of his head, and will need to dip himself seven times in de Jordan afore he is clean.' "

"Well, Rastus," I said, how about the rest of the slaves, are many of them here in heaven?"

"Oh," he said, "dear Mr. Sodi, I 'spects you haven't recognized dem since they have put on their shinin' garments and put off de black ones. There's multitudes of dem here and dey sing in de choir wid de odder people and their voices are often de loudest. Of course, dey are not all here by any means. Many of dem were as big hypocrites as de master. Some were of de fearful kind; some of de unbelievin' sort; and some were de whoremongers and de liars. And God says all these shall have their part in de lake of fire and brimstone. If I could only go back and see dem once more, I would take dis harp and show dem dis robe, and take 'em one bunch of de fruit; dey might believe me, though dey would not believe Moses and de prophets."

"Well, Rastus, the visit has been very interesting to me."

"And to me also," said Rastus, "but my company is scattering and I must also go, and will see you again soon, I trust." So saying he said good-bye and disappeared among the chariots, and thousands who were leaving the martyrs' reunion.

I now said to mother: "It does seem a most blessed thing that there are no feelings of prejudice here toward anyone whom God sees fit to enter the gates."

"Oh," she said, "we are here from every nation under heaven, all races, kindreds, tongues and people are here; and all are in the likeness of their Lord. While all retain a peculiar likeness to their former life."

"But see, David's chariot is coming." In a few moments we were seated with him and flying with great speed toward the city gate. We passed in at the gate of Manasseh and at last halted near the children's great polytechnic. Mother and Mary stepped out and I bade them good-bye for the present, saying, "I hope to see you again soon," for David had said, "I will take you on a flying trip through some of the leading avenues toward the throne, for I see your heart is in that direction and I have a commission to be your servant for a time."

On we went through streets and avenues, flying at unmeasured speed. The light of the throne began to be luminous in the distance, even the trees lining the thoroughfares, somewhat like the trees for shade in earthly cities, seemed hanging with diamonds and rubies of glistening brightness and the mansions seemed literally studded with the same.

We now came to a broad avenue leading toward the throne. Thousands of glorified saints, some walking, engaged in holy conversation, others in the chariots, with the joy and rest of heaven upon them, were going toward and from the throne.

I now turned to David and said: "While I am anxious to go on to the throne, I am very eager to see the dear bosom companion of my life, who I am told is detained in a distant place in paradise."

"Oh," said David, "why did you not tell me while we were in paradise? We could have gone so quickly; but now I will turn the chariot, and go at once, for I know her well and she will be greatly pleased, and I myself will be greatly pleased in assisting you for this great pleasure trip. So turning his chariot, he said, "Have you any choice of routes?"

"Not any, for I know nothing of the way, only go past the children's polytechnic and take mother and Mary. I am so ignorant of the ways, so choose for me."

"Most gladly indeed," said David. So with the speed of sound we were flying toward the great cathedral, and soon halted beside the gate."

Seneca now said: "You have written enough for this night. Transcribe all carefully and I will see you again as usual," and so bade me good night.

CHAPTER TWENTY-TWO

Eleventh Visit
Another Visit into Paradise with Mother and Daughter
Meets the Wife of His Youth

(I freely confess that by this time I was so carried away by the wonderful revelations of Seneca Sodi, that I could scarcely think of anything else, day or night, and after he would leave me of nights I would dream I was in heaven and walking the same streets where I had gone in vision and on waking felt disappointment that I was not there.)

But it was now time for his return. My manuscript and everything was ready. Really, I was eager for his coming, for I was anxious indeed for another trip into paradise and further to see how saints in heaven assist each other. A rap was heard on the door and Seneca came in.

"Good evening," he said, and came and gripped my hand with that peculiar touch that only the hand of a spiritual body can impart.

I welcomed him to a seat, but he said: "Where is your manuscript?" He hastily looked it over, with a smile and nod of approval, "only," he said, "I fear we have not put the soul and spirit of my concern into the message as we should have done. The eager concern I have that it may stamp itself upon all who read, that they may feel the importance of a due and rightful preparation for the life to come, for men do not know what they are doing when they trifle with the vast concerns of an eternal scene, but when you, dear son, have done your best, God will bless your effort and mine, for it has been sent."

After I again assured him I would do all I could to faithfully declare his message, he took his seat near me and began as follows:

We closed our last meeting while in David's chariot at the gateway of the children's great amphitheater and were planning a tour to a distant point in paradise. I was eager to see my bosom companion who was busily engaged with a thousand more, as I had been told, assisting a great number of souls who had recently come into the heavenly realm from certain heathen countries where the missionaries had been busily preaching the Lord Jesus. So, as we were waiting in the chariot, I saw my mother and Mary passing near, and beckoned them to us. When I told them of my great desire and David's pleasing offer, they at once accepted our invitation to go along with us and were soon seated by our side.

Mother at once said: "I know well where they are, at one of the remote stations far beyond the gate of Benjamin." So David turned the chariot to the right, saying, "I will go down Ninety-second Avenue and out at the gate of Benjamin."

No sweeter raptures filled my soul since leaving the Judean gate at our first entrance into the city, and where we had been welcomed by the Lord of the kingdom. The thoughts of the family reunion were so precious. Mother and daughter by my side. David the sweet singer of Israel, our servant. He who had led the hosts of the servants of the Most High and fought His battles, now our servant and so soon to meet the dear wife of my youth who has for many years been so prominent in these eternal realms in service for her Lord. Oh, blessed morning it was to me! My whole soul was in raptures of delight with the sweet thought.

David now said: "Are you ready?" and the chariot moved on. We were now passing through a new section of the city to me. Mother and Mary seemed to be much at home and acquainted with the route.

Mary now spoke and said: "Father, I am so glad you can so soon see dear mother, she has been so busy of late, she has not had time to visit with me, as we often do, but we will soon meet, and I can introduce you. I wonder if she will know you amidst all the busy throng."

"Know me! Oh, yes. How could she help knowing me? I have changed but little since we parted. Indeed, dear child, I am very eager to see her myself, even more than you can know, for you have had no separations from any loved ones. Neither have you known the sorrows and tears which we have known so long. All these you escaped, as well as the dark sins of the world. I do not think now we ought to have grieved so much and so long as we did when you left us, for you were eternally safe from that moment."

"Oh, indeed, I am safe and very happy in my experience. I know nothing of the sorrow and tears of which you speak. Others have often told me of their sad mistakes and sin-burdened hearts: but how thankful they all are, for our blessed Redeemer! Without Him I would have been lost myself and would never have seen nor entered this celestial world."

David began to slacken the speed of the chariot, and, calling me by my name, said: "I want you to notice what we are now passing."

On both sides of the great avenue there were multitudes of peculiar, yet most beautifully constructed mansions.

"These," said David, "are built according to the tastes and fancies of their occupants, as indeed all the 'many mansions' are. You have noticed the great variety of scenery and buildings throughout the city, no doubt. Everyone can choose his own; and change to another at his own will. God Himself delights in variety and has made no two blades of grass alike, neither two grains of sand, nor two human souls. But communities in the world with similar choices — education and fancies, naturally group together here, so you see in these peculiar mansions. You will notice how happy and contented everyone seems to be in this great colony."

Mother now spoke and said to David: "I have been here for many years and yet I have never seen anyone dissatisfied or restless or homesick. It seems our great Father has anticipated all the wishes and desires of all His people and has so planned and arranged this eternal kingdom that everyone has his desires fully met in all things."

"The city," said David, "with all its variety of architecture and constructions, its fruits and rivers and fountains, is adapted to all the nations of the earth; and from all the nations, kindreds, people and tongues, these countless numbers are gathered. Multitudes from heathen nations are here, their children especially, in large numbers are here, for they do not arrive to the age of accountability so early as in Christian lands. These are all saved by virtue of the atonement, until they sin against eternal light; so thousands are gathered here well grown in years and it is these that are being taught, by these faithful servants, in the preparatory regions of paradise, to which point we are now going."

"Oh, David, " I said, "will you speed your chariot, for I am eager to meet her who was the bosom companion of my life on earth?"

With this the chariot flew as with the speed of sound. The

96

avenue was a perfect pleasure ground of delight. Trees loaded with their ripening fruit! Beautiful mansions of all descriptions! Thousands of happy souls, going and coming! Many reclining on the cushioned upholstery of heaven! But with the speed we were now going thousands of mansions were passed without distinguishing one from another.

"I see the gateway in the distance," said Mary.

"Are we so near the great wall and the entrance into paradise?" I said.

I looked up to scan the great wall again, with its magnificent splendors, as David was slowing his chariot. The gate stood open as indeed they all do. As we passed out at the gate of Benjamin with its great glistening pearl and shining hinges of gold, we had only time to cast one glance backward to say good-bye to the city, until we seemed to be many leagues beyond, along one of the great highways of paradise.

Mary leaned her head upon my shoulder and said: "Father, how do you like the music and hum of the chariot wheels? Ordinarily they are almost noiseless."

"Oh, I am bewildered at the immensity and grandeur of heaven. Mother, how soon do you think we will reach our station?"

"Oh, quite soon, I think I see the domes and steeples of the mission now."

"Yes," said Mary, "they are quite plain to me."

"Oh, glory!" I said. "Look at the mountains, hills, and valleys we are passing. Oh, my soul is perfectly full of rapture. Oh, for a thousand tongues—."

"Use the one you have," said Mary.

"Hallelujah to God!" I shouted, when David quickly took his harp and we all sang again the victories of the Lamb.

The chariot now stood still outside a great archway leading to one of the preparatory departments in paradise. We all stepped out when to my surprise more than a hundred most beautiful spirits met us, all with the glory and light of heaven upon them. Introduction? I needed none—especially to one— the fairest among the hundred, and altogether lovely. She sprang from among the rest and shouted: "Glory to God in the highest!" She fell on my neck but could not weep, neither could I , for none can weep in heaven; but the cup of our joy was full.

"I knew you were coming," said Genevive, "but did not know David would bring you. Oh, how glad I am you are now at home! And then here's mother and daughter," she said, as she clasped them both in her arms.

"Dear Genevive, I have been anxious to see you ever since coming into paradise, but could not reach you earlier. Our dreams of the future while on earth are now realized; our prayers answered. Home at last!"

"Oh," said Genevive, "I have much to ask you, so we will walk to yonder group of buildings."

David said, "my time is at your disposal. Take your leisure, for so I have command."

As we walked slowly along I was introduced to many of those who met us at the gateway. I found they were from various parts of the world; but all were engaged in a blessed service for our Lord. Everyone seemed perfectly joyful and happy.

"Now," said Seneca, "You must rest for a few minutes, and while you rest will you share in the fruit of my basket?" I put out my hand to take what seemed a beautiful orange, but I could not grasp it. I seemed mortified to think he was eating and I could not.

"Why is it?" I said.

"This fruit," said he, "Is but a tiny sample of what I have been telling you about. You will not forget that the heavenly world is a spiritual kingdom, and all things have a spiritual trend, and truly you can only eat of this fruit after you have crossed the boundary of your earthly habitation."

CHAPTER TWENTY-THREE

Eleventh Visit — Continued
Seneca's Further Visit with His Wife, Mother and Daughter

"You may now write again," said Seneca.

We were now within a most beautiful building — a large drawing room or parlor, beautifully decorated with various kinds of ornaments unlike what I was used to seeing within the gates of the city. Everything was tinged with silver drapings, lovely indeed; and the upholstery of chairs, sofas, etc. was of magnificent designs of heavenly patterns.

From this room we were brought into the large spacious dining hall which was fairly ablaze with burnished silver hangings and all manner of silver-tinged table ware. Think of a table three thousand cubits long, at which ten thousand guests can sit down at one time and you have some idea of this dining hall.

Genevive now came and said: "We will go to yonder side table where we can sit down together." So Genevive, Mary, mother and myself were seated alone, while David and all who met us at the gate were gone on to the farther end of the great hall.

Genevive now ordered our luncheon which consisted of beautiful cakes of the finest of the wheat of paradise, with all manner of fruit with which paradise abounds everywhere. Breadfruit grows in abundance and is one of the twelve kinds on each tree. When our thanksgiving was over, Genevive, who sat by my side, said to me: "I have been anxious for this time to come when we should all be together again and the sorrows of earth be past. Now tell me about the rest of the children."

"Yes," said Mary, "tell us all about them. I am so anxious to know about my brothers and sisters of whom mother says there are six."

"I am glad to tell you they are all alive and getting on well in the world and in homes of their own. They are not all good Christians and yet they have all known the way of life and we trust they will yet all be counted among the saved."

"Oh, yes," said Genevive, "I have so often prayed for them and yonder angel which you see with David and the rest has often told me about them, for he often visits the sections of earth where they live."

"How often I have wondered with anxiety, if the saints in heaven know about the affairs and doings of those they have left behind, and your words, Genevive, thoroughly convince me that they do."

"True, indeed," said Genevive, "we have frequent messages from the earth."

"Oh, Genevive, there is no comparison between the humble fare of our earthly table and what we have here. How refreshed I feel, and then those wonderful fountains in the distance, gushing up from burnished silver fixtures, and hundreds gathering about them drinking to their hearts' content!" Oh, heaven, indeed! How precious that promise: "He shall lead them to living fountains of water!"

"This is its fulfilment," said Genevive, "and when you see the ten thousand at these tables with the bounties of heaven before them then you'll say, "The Lamb which is in the midst of the throne shall feed them," for truly all this blessed provision and infinitely more than what we can see here, is the gracious result of His thoughtful care of His people, for He hath prepared for them a city."

"Now," said Mary to Genevive, "I wish you would take us through the great amphitheater."

We all arose and followed as Genevive led the way. A doorway opened from the great dining hall into a stupendous apartment, furnished with seats somewhat like the ancient amphitheater of the world. Thousands were seated in various places of this great building. Silver furnishings were everywhere sparkling with the glory of paradise. This great hall I found to be one of the places where are gathered the heathen who have been saved by Christ and are yet uninstructed in the ways of the kingdom or in spiritual matters in reference to salvation. One of the chief stations of paradise opening its doors to heathen countries is just near this place."

Genevive now said: "I always took a great interest in mission work in the world, in Sunday school and children's classes, and the same traits are with me here. Of my own choice I spend much time instructing the precious souls who come to these portals, ignorant of God's plans and purposes. All the heathen infants are saved as well as those in civilized and Christian lands. Their accountability is not reached in as early years as they are

100

in more enlightened nations, hence a larger number die in childhood and youth, who have never known the law of God to bring them under condemnation; and being under the free gift with eternal life, they are gathered here in very great ignorance. While heathen nations are responsible to God, yet their responsibility is not so great as those of Christian lands."

"But, mother," said Mary, "how is it that so many of the heathen children are saved and gathered here when so many of their parents are lost?"

"Their parents," said Genevive, "have reached an age of accountability through the measure of light they have. They have likewise sinned and fallen under condemnation and following their superstitions have died in their sins, while their children have not reached the place of enlightenment to bring them under such responsibility."

At this I spoke and said, "The Bible declares that 'By the transgression of one man judgment came upon all men to condemnation. Even so, by the righteousness of one man the free gift came upon all men to justification of life.' (Romans 5:18) So in man's beginning he is universally saved by Christ, as Paul said again, 'I was alive without the law once, but when the commandment came sin revived and I died.' "

"Indeed," said Genevive. "All are alive and remain so until they receive a knowledge of God's will sufficient to bring them under responsibility, when by transgression spiritual death follows. But I see you are eager to know about this great place for the gathering of the hosts of those saved by Christ from heathen lands. Do you notice what a large proportion are young people and children? These have had but little instruction in the ways of the true God, His worship and spiritual nature; many of them none at all. Their teaching of idolatry clings to them and they must be trained in the ways and truths of the eternal kingdom.

"Each of these has a history of its own. They wonder with great astonishment as to who and where they are, when the angels have brought them within the gates of paradise. The shining glory of this world is so great, many of them are completely overcome, like one on earth just awakened from a sleep filled with an enchanting dream, they are speechless with wonder. Little children of different ages are here and yet many of these know as much as children of Christian lands. This great

amphitheater is often filled until every seat is taken and here
they are taught everything pertaining to an earlier experience in
this world of light. Many of them were objects of scorn and
neglect, without friends or a mother's love. They greatly
admire and wonder at the kindness shown them here.
Thousands and millions of them have gone throughout the
regions of paradise and into the city and their voices are ringing
out with the melody of heaven."

"Genevive," I said, "why is this place arranged for the
heathen more than for any others?"

"It is not for heathen children alone," she replied. "There
are many here from Christian lands; but God has made wise
provisions for all His people. The teaching here is adapted to a
class who hardly know the rudiments of anything in modern or
civilized life, and who know nothing of the doctrines of
salvation. Many of those boys and girls and even men and
women whom you see are being taught in those classes yonder,
are only as those in the chart class, in the schools of the world.
The great effort is to instruct them and develop their spiritual
and intellectual faculties. It is most interesting to note how
rapidly they develop from mere babes into full-fledged saints in
heaven.

"They all quickly learn to praise God and everyone has a
harp similar to your own. The great praise services which are
held here very frequently are soul-refreshing seasons, I assure
you. When twenty thousand to thirty thousand all join in the
new songs so recently learned, and quoting passages and
heavenly teaching concerning the eternal truths of God, much
as we did on earth in our praise services, these arches and domes
echo and re-echo the melody until you would think the vi-
brations would be heard in the city itself."

"Well, Genevive, I cannot tell you how much I have enjoyed
this meeting and visit with you. My whole soul is filled with
the highest sense of adoring praise to our Lord, for such love
tokens for His people. Surely, all these great things for the
children He had in mind before the foundation of the world was
laid."

"Indeed," said Genevive, "or even before this paradise was
planned or fitted up."

"Well, dear Genevive, are you engaged here so constantly
that you cannot go to other places when you would like to do

so?"

"Oh, no," she replied, "I have the most unbounded freedom, even as that of the angels or the elders themselves, to go as I will, and I will be exceedingly glad to accompany you to any places you wish to go."

"Oh, Genevive, nothing could give me more pleasure than to have you go with us. I was just planning a visit to the throne itself when I felt I must see you first and David generously offered his services and our party was quickly made up, as you see."

"If you would like," said Genevie, "I will go with you to the throne and we can return at our leisure to this or other parts of paradise." So she called mother and Mary to us and made the proposition which was quickly accepted. She dispatched one standing nearby to bring David and the hundred, and in a few moments they were with us.

I said to David: "We have decided to return at once to the city and to go on toward the throne."

"I am at your pleasure until this trip is ended."

Genevive quickly arranged for others to fill her place in the great preparatory classes, saying we must now join with the rest in a chorus of thanksgiving, ere we leave the amphitheater. The order of the services was quickly arranged. David led in the chorus. We had tuned our harps and joined with them, and falling on our faces, with adoring praises, we fairly shouted the salvation of God. We now arose and with deep emotions said good-bye to the great hosts we were leaving behind. We walked toward the gateway where stood the chariot. After saying once again good-bye to those beautiful spirits of light, with the pure love tokens of which heaven abounds, we were seated in the chariot.

"Now," said Seneca, as he turned to me, "you may rest for the night. Faithfully transcribe and make the message plain." He turned his back and with a pleasant good-night, disappeared from my room.

CHAPTER TWENTY-FOUR

Twelfth Visit
The Return to the City — Going on to the Throne

At the appointed hour Seneca came in. He seemd to hasten to his usual place for his story left him sitting in the chariot at our last meeting.

"My son, have you everything ready for the message?"
"I have," I replied, and he proceeded as follows:

David now said: "Have you a choice of routes? A thousand leagues are between us and the city gates."

Genevive quickly spoke and said: "Let us go by way of the gorge route including the cliffs, for I remember, Mr. Sodi was very fond of natural scenery and especially that of a mountainous and stupendous character."

"I am sure, father, you will have your desire fully met," said Mary. "I do not know what the world was like or its moutains and rivers, but I have gone this route a few times with mother and grandmother, as well as others, and I know you will be pleased."

"Indeed, I am sure I will. And Genevive, dear, I am glad you remember my natural inclinations and have made this choice for my proclivities linger with me yet."

David's chariot began to tremble as a thing of life again. We turned to the many standing at the gateway and said good-bye, until we meet you again.

I found that Genevive had a host of friends, for thousands had gathered to see her off, and to sing a parting hymn; the chorus I still remember:

> "We only say good-bye in heaven,
> Assured to meet again.
> God's blessing guide you all the way
> By mountain, vale, or glen."

As the chariot moved away, they soon faded from our sight in the distance behind. Beautiful fields with teeming harvests were spread out in a great valley before us.

Mother spoke, and said: "Not a drop of human sweat was

104

needed to produce these fields of golden harvests. There is no curse here — no weeds nor briars, but our good Father's will makes all provision for us. Yet notwithstanding everything grows in heaven without human toil and sweat, yet men are employed to gather in these great harvests and the labor is but a kind of picnic for joy."

"Oh, how much," I replied, "is wrapped up in God's love to man!" Beautiful flowers of endless varieties were lining the chariot's pathway. "The fragrance from the fields and flowers is so exhilarating, my soul is filled with raptures of delight," I cried. Oh, why do men in the world put so little value on God's revelation of this great pleasure ground of eternal delight? Many Christian people there are who try to believe that heaven is only a state of rest and quietude of soul forever, and do not think of it as a place of such magnificent glory. Such rob themselves of the joy of expectation; and hope is not the anchor it would be if their faith and hope were after God's ideas and revelations.

We now came in sight of beautiful buildings in the distance. So I said to Genevive: "What are those buildings we see yonder?"

"Just a village of paradise," she said, "many of the inhabitants have mansions also in the city, but often spend much of their time here, as these pleasure grounds are greatly appreciated."

David slackened the speed of the chariot as we passed through its streets. Beautiful fountains were beside the driveway and so were the trees with their ripening fruit.

David halted beside a gushing fountain, we all sprang from the chariot and with silver goblets were refreshed with the water of life. After selecting such fruit as we needed we were again in the chariot, which moved on with slackened speed, for the scenery was too grand to be hastily passed by.

Soon the hills and mountains far in the distance before us came in view. A lovely river winding about the foothills was also plain to be seen. On we passed. Deep gorges between the hills and spurs of the mountains lent their enchantment to the scene. The roadway was now winding among this gorgeous mountain scenery. The chariot was climbing the mountain sides, so as to pass over the high mountain valleys.

David now turned to me and said: "My son, I am delighted to have this opportunity of driving through this stupendous mountain route, nor do I ever tire of it. It reminds me when I used to hide in the caves and among the rocks and mountains when fleeing from Saul, my persecutor. Those were times never to be forgotten. I have often looked but in vain hoping I might see Saul coming in a chariot along some of the great mountain roads of paradise, but I have never met him nor have I heard any word concerning his presence within the gates of paradise or the city itself."

"Poor Saul," I said, "he rejected God's word and denied obedience to Him, and the penalty must be paid."

I now looked up to the vast overhanging crags above us and again downward to the deep gorges of thousands of feet below. At different places along this roadway were beautiful pleasure grounds so when or wherever any desired, they could alight from the chariot and enjoy strolls among beautiful shrubbery and all manner of trees bearing fruit. At one of these David brought the chariot to a standstill, and we all gathered beneath the wide spreading branches of one of the trees of life and began to gather of its fruit. I felt so full of thanksgiving to God that I fairly shouted: "What hath God wrought! Oh, David, tell me, how vast is this great paradise?"

"Oh," said David, "there is plenty of room in heaven for all the millions that ever have been or ever will be born. These pleasure grounds are almost limitless. I do not know the utmost bounds of heaven: possibly Enoch, Abraham or Moses can tell. One thing I can tell, there is no sin, no sorrow, nor death here. There is no evil-minded person in all this vast domain. Nothing that worketh abomination or maketh a lie ever enters within the gates of the city or even paradise itself."

At this David went to the chariot and bringing his harp said: "We must now join in a song of thanksgiving." We quickly took our harps from our girdles and tuned them with David's. He began with the word of the thirty-third Psalm, thinking I knew it best. Then we all sang:

"Rejoice in the Lord, O ye righteous: for praise is comely for the upright.
Praise the Lord with harp: sing unto Him with the psaltery and an instrument of ten strings.

Sing unto Him a new song; play skillfully with a loud noise. For the word of the Lord is right, and all His works are done in truth.

By the word of the Lord were the heavens made, and all the host of them by the breath of His mouth."

When we had finished this song of thanksgiving, David said: "No doubt, you will meet Nehemiah, one of the dear saints of heaven, who wrote while on earth, as I remember, under divine inspiration, and said: "Thou even thou art Lord alone; thou hast made heaven, the heaven of heavens, with all their hosts; the earth and all things that are therein, the sea and all that is therein, and thou preservest them all; and the hosts of heaven worship thee.' " (Nehemiah 9:6)

He continued: "Angels from this heavenly world visit the earth in great numbers and sometimes saints have the privilege as well, but of this I will speak to you at another time."

"Oh, how blessed to know," I replied, "that I belong to Him: that I was converted, became as a little child, believed in Jesus, humbled myself, was born again, received eternal life, and now have this great exaltation! Oh, hallelujah to God!" I cried.

Genevive said:"Shall we not now go on, for there are many things yet on the way to the city?"

We were soon seated in the chariot and David touched the magic button and the chariot moved along, rolling on in the mighty ascent toward the mountain summit. Off in the distance could be seen peak after peak and mountain after mountain; everything glittering with the glory of God upon it. Still we moved on and mounted higher and higher, spanning immense gorges on causeways built by the Lord of the Kingdom Himself. To one unaccustomed, it seemed both a dizzy and dangerous route.

I said to Genevive, "Are we entirely safe with such prodigious heights, and such speed as we are making?"

"Safe! Dangerous route!" she said, "there are no dangers in heaven. Accidents , there are none. Mistakes are few as we soon learn the deeper wisdom of God."

We passed many chariot loads going in the direction from whence we had just come. All were so cheerful and happy. We always gave and received a pleasant salute as the chariots passed each other with slackened speed. Nearly always the newcomers like myself would shout out with a wave of the hand: "Home at last, home at last!"

We met one chariot upon the summit of this great range, guided by Elijah, filled with men and women with a half dozen children besides new arrivals from the world, but a happier group I hardly ever saw. David threw out a signal and both chariots stood still side by side. We greeted each other with handshakes and kisses of true love. The children were so full of glee and joyous wonder. Like myself, this was their first trip over this wonderful gorge route. They asked us many questions and seemed eager to go on. No thought of fear, but with perfect confidence in their elders, and Elijah's guiding hand, they seemed entirely satisfied. After passing them a basket of fruit which we had gathered, they thanked us and their chariot moved on.

David said: "Now we must hasten on for there are interesting things just before us." So on we went, mounting still higher. We soon came to a most lovely park on the plateau high upon the mountain summit. Into this park David guided his chariot. We sat a moment spellbound at the lovely scenery. Groves of heavenly fruit-bearing trees, flowering shrubbery of many kinds, roadways winding in all directions, with a great number of chariots much like David's standing here and there, with others slowly moving about filled with joyous souls — men, women and children — all happy and enjoying this heavenly pleasure ground to the full. "Sure enough," I said, "what hath God wrought for His people!"

David now brought his chariot to a halt. Many of the great host turned toward us, recognizing David, the king. In a few moments a great company had gathered near, saluting David and us. But "who are the strangers," they wondered. We were soon introduced and greeted afresh. David now said: "Take your leisure, go where you wish."

We took a long stroll, meeting hundreds who like myself were here for the first time. The great pleasure park was fifteen or twenty furlongs on each side. Numerous fountains were located at different places and were the sources of innumerable rivers and streams in paradise, and a part of the great system which flows from the city and from the throne itself on the banks of which, both in the Holy City and throughout all paradise, grow the trees of life with their twelve manner of fruit. A table in the center was literally covered with this delightful fruit of paradise of which we all ate freely, while enjoying this most interesting visit.

"Well, my son," said mother, "are you repaid for your efforts and self-denial in the Lord's service in the world?"

"Oh, mother, why do you ask me that question? I am a thousand times repaid already. Just what I see and enjoy now here in this park is ample reward for all the toil of an earth's pilgrimage. But who are those two men coming toward us?"

Mother said: "I do not recognize them."

Genevive said: "They are strangers, perhaps recently come into paradise." By this time they were near us. They had locked arms and were walking together in a joyous conversation. They attracted my attention, for I seemed to recognize them both. "Hello, good morning," and in a moment we were clasping each other in our arms and with high praises to God we were shouting, "Glory to God in the highest!" But who were they? Only two of my friends whom I had learned to know and to love many years ago, one Mr. Fuggele of Stavanger, Norway, and the other dear soul was my friend Mr. Ransome, of London, England.

"Oh, brethren," I shouted, "I see you are here, but I had not heard that you had left the world. Oh, Brother Fuggele, the last time we met on earth, we wept together in the railroad station in your native town, and Brother Edwin Ransome, you were a father to me when I was in your great city of London. Well, brethren, I am truly glad to meet you here. I have only been here a short time and have not yet been to the throne; but oh, I am overwhelmed with the greatness and glory of this celestial world."

Edwin Ransome now said: "We have been here for quite a while, but never have been to this great pleasure ground before. Isn't it grand?" he said.

"This beats the mountains of Norway," said Brother Fuggele. "I thought they were grand enough, although snow covered and frozen with the ice like the frigid zone, in midsummer, but here the prodigious heights of these delectable mountains know nothing but the spring mornings of heaven. Surely, no cold blasts ever sweep over these mountain tops."

"No," I shouted, "for just see these trees of giant growth, hanging with their golden fruits, like the luxuriant clusters of the tropical lands of the earth. No winter ever comes here, I am sure."

At this there came a group of happy men, precious souls, passing near us. I said, "Who are they?" and they were quickly invited to tarry a moment for an introduction. My friends, Edwin Ransome and Peter Fuggele, knew them well, and said: "They are a group of ministers who were noted and well-known in the world, greatly beloved on earth and so they are in heaven."

I was soon introduced to Christmas Evans and Rowland Hill of England, Dr. Guthrie also. Robert Flockhart and John Wesley stood side by side. Dr. Adam Clark and George Fox were also introduced, then there came Peter Cartwright and Lorenzo Dow, with many others.

"Oh," I cried and said, "I have heard and read of all you good men. Glad indeed, very glad I am to meet you all here. This must be the 'preachers' picnic party.'" I beckoned to mother, Genevive and Mary, who also came and were introduced. A number of seats were brought and placed beneath the broad, spreading branches of the tree and we all sat down, when we saw David coming toward us carrying his harp. When he had come near, all these brethren arose and greeted him with a most heavenly welcome. David made a most courteous bow and with a pleasant smile was seated with us. Then standing and taking in the situation, he quickly introduced his chariot group again when they arose and gave us another welcome. At this I arose and said: "Dear brethren, my soul is so overcome with the joy and gladness of heaven, I cannot longer restrain my feelings."

"Don't try longer," said Rowland Hill, but let us all praise God together. We knelt, and such a praise service I hardly ever witnessed, especially of such intense feelings and raptures of joy. George Fox seemed to praise God louder and sweeter than most anyone else. At last we arose and David started a hymn, playing upon his harp. We all joined and sang with him. After much conversation we decided that all would go together to the farther side of the park. David led the way and we all followed. We soon found that many of these blessed men had not visited this place nor passed over this route for a long time so it seemed as new to them as to us. Again I said to Genevive: "I am glad you chose this route for our return trip to the city. Oh, such glorious things as are in store for us!" We soon came to the outer limits of the park where we found ourselves on the very summit of a great mountain range in paradise. As we stood and looked off in the far distance over the foothills and down through immense valleys and plains, we seemed lost in wonder. In the beautiful clear atmosphere of heaven we could see great distances over and into the valleys many leagues below us. The roadways winding down the mountain side with such a variety of trees on their borders rendered the scene before us without a parallel in all creation. As I stood looking over this wonder, I said to David with the words of the Queen of Sheba: "The half has never been told me," (I Kings 10:7) and again, "Eye hath not seen, nor ear heard, neither hath it entered into the heart of man, the things which God hath prepared for them that love him." (I Corinthians 2:9) As we looked far down into the valley as well as along the mountain slopes we could see an innumerable number of mansions and temporary residences of those who preferred to spend much of their time in those regions. I thought again of our Lord's words: "I go to prepare a place for you, that where I am, there ye may be also, and oh, what provision He has made! (John 14:2)

Genevive now came and said: "Mr. Sodi, is your curiosity satisfied?"

"Satisfied! Is any soul not satisfied here? I have climbed to the top of many of the highest mountains of the earth, but they were only mole hills compared to these wonders of paradise, and then just think, these are here forever. Ours to enjoy always! No sickness! No old age! No death, sorrow nor crying! Redeemed and saved forever! Oh, Genevive, I am so glad we are here! Oh what glorious heights of elevation to which we are raised! Only a little while ago we were in the world subject to sickness, sorrow and death. Now all this is passed. No more death! But in heaven, equal to the angels, and with the saved of all ages!"

David now came and said: "We have need to be on our journey," and so, bidding our holy brethren good-bye, we returned to the chariot. After gathering our needed supply of fruit and drinking again from the gushing fountain we were quickly seated in David's chariot preparatory for our journey to the city of the great King. We sung a hymn of praise for these great wonders. As soon as we had begun to sing many hundreds gathered quickly when they saw David standing in the chariot with his harp and joined with us in loud hallelujahs to God.

Just at this moment came two lovely women, inviting us to tarry a little and dine with them at their table nearby. They knew David well and asked concerning us; we quickly introduced ourselves, when Mary recognized them both and sprang from the chariot and embraced them in her arms, saying: "Oh, Emma dear, and Susie, how glad I am to see you!" These, I found had been her companions in their infancy in heaven. "Oh," she says, "father, these were my chums in our girlhood experiences." Of course, we went with them for they knew David also.

They, like ourselves, were just picnicking for a brief time on this mountain summit. They had gathered many kinds of fruit and a beautiful table was loaded with all that any soul could wish. Surely we enjoyed this feast as souls only can who have passed the boundaries of earthly lives into the new unions and fellowships of the life eternal. We thanked them for the pleasant entertainment and bidding them good-bye were soon in the chariot again.

CHAPTER TWENTY-FIVE

Twelfth Visit — Continued

So the chariot moved on leaving the mountain scenery behind us. Our route now was through a broad but beautiful valley. We could see such great distances before us in the clear light of paradise. The great orchards, orange and lemon groves of the world were but miniature garden spots to what now opened before us.

As we made our descent from the heights behind us there was spread out as far as the eye could reach on either side immense groves of fruit-bearing trees of all kinds and descriptions, interspersed with most lovely flowers such as I had never seen before.

"Oh, where are we?" I cried, "I am bewildered with this magnificent glory and wonderful provision of our God." I fell on my face. Genevive and Mary both joined me and blessed aloud the God of our being. "Oh, God, thou Maker of all! Oh, Lord Jesus, thou Redeemer and Saviour, with high thanksgiving we pour out our souls to Thee! Eternal praise shall be Thine forever."

When we arose, my mother said: "From these regions vast supplies are taken into the city. Look," said she, "at those trainloads yonder."

"Wonderful," I said, as I saw hundreds busily loading them with the choicest fruit and spiritual vegetables of all kinds.

A hundred leagues of these groves were passed. I saw many thousands of happy spirits gathering fruit from these orchards of beauty and trainloads were frequently leaving enroute for the city.

Genevive now said: "Do you see the light of the city yonder?"

"Oh, indeed," I shouted. "I think it must be the sunrise of a June morning in heaven."

"How well you have judged," said David. "The Son of God, the Lamb Himself, is the light thereof. June morning always! There is no winter here." In a few moments the wall of the city came into view, and the gate of Simeon loomed up before us.

"Oh, David, slacken thy speed, give us more time to see and consider the greatness of this mighty wall, and to read again the names of the foundations on which it stands, ere we pass in at the gate of Simeon."

The angel of the gate threw up his hands with a lovely welcome. I said to Genevive: "Why do the angels guard the gateways bearing the names of the twelve tribes of Israel?"

"Oh," said she, "had it not been for the twelve tribes of ancient Israel paving this way before us and giving us the alphabet, spelling the eternal mysteries of God, such an abundant entrance into the city we would never have known. But like Israel when plodding their way to their ancient capital and the annual feasts we would have had no better equipments than they, and with the increasing numbers gathering at these gates they would be blocked and jammed to our utter confusion. So the angel is stationed just to guide the hosts, to preserve perfect order, and to welcome all who are prepared for the blessedness of the city and the mansions. Ignorance is no bar to entrance at the gates but an unlikeness to the blessed face of Jesus is; so the angel's presence and judgment decides."

"So," said Genevive, "ancient Israel opened the way: went before all of us Gentiles. God had prepared for them a city and they looked forward with longing eyes toward their inheritance."

"Oh, indeed, Genevive dear, I remember a precious word of the Bible which we used to love so much while on earth. Speaking of Abraham, it says: "For he looked for a city which hath foundations whose builder and maker is God." (Hebrews 11:10)

"How true," said Genevive, "these ancient saints died in faith, full of the promises of God, which they saw afar off. And they were persuaded of them and embraced them and so confessed they were strangers and pilgrims in the earth, desiring a better country, that was this heavenly one. So God was not ashamed to be called their God because He had built for them this city." (Hebrews 11:13-16)

"Oh, how true!" I said. "And none but the true and eternal God could have build such a city as this for them and us."

David's chariot had been standing still for some time during this conversation and he had been quietly listening. He now turned to us and said: "I have been delighted with the course of your conversation. For hundreds of years before the Gentile period came in, thousands of the Jews crowded at these gates.

We were most all Jews then; but now the Gentiles are far out-stripping us: but then the Gentiles are our brethren for they are Abraham's seed after all and heirs of the promise. But we must now pass along." The chariot moved slowly under the archway of the great gate. The angel waved us good-bye as we left the wondrous gate and wall behind.

Mother now spoke and said to David: "Kindly guide the chariot to the children's cathedral."

I said to her: "Are you eager to see the little ones again?"

"I am always delighted to be with them, but I want to assure you I have greatly enjoyed this entire trip." We all said the same, but no one had enjoyed it like myself: everything was so new, so wonderful, never to be forgotten.

"Now, David, the avenue seems broad here, hasten with what speed you wish." He reached out his hand and pressed the button again, when the chariot seemed to fly with the wings of the light. In a few moments we were slowing up beside the gateway of the Polytechnic. We all alighted and thanked David for his kindly services, who turned and said: "I am always glad to do you such a favor."

David now moved his chariot to the further side of the street and was gathering some fruit, while we were busy talking over the wonderful journey we had just completed."

Seneca Sodi now said: "I leave you, my son, for a little rest."

I threw myself back in my chair with my eyes closed and reverently thanked my God for such revelations of the unseen world.

"Oh, how real is the future life," I said. "I devoutly wish I was there now. No trouble, no sorrow, no death. Oh, heaven, not far away, may thy gates be opened for me, and may the angel's chariot hasten to my humble cot!" I thus mused and prayed until I was fast asleep.

CHAPTER TWENTY-SIX

Twelfth Visit — Continued
On to the Throne — Jonah, the Prophet

Seneca Sodi returned and said: "You may write again," and he proceeded as follows:

Genevive, mother and Mary were standing at the gateway. David's chariot was standing on the opposite side of the avenue, where he was still gathering some fruit and filling a basket. I saw Bohemond also coming toward us, and beckoned him to hasten.

"Oh, Bohemond, I have many things to tell you. Many blessed things have occurred since we parted. I want to introduce to you my bosom companion, the wife of my youth, whom I have just found most busily engaged in a distant part of paradise."

Genevive seemed greatly pleased to know we were such close friends.

Bohemond now said: "When are you going on to the throne?"

"Oh, very soon, I trust."

Genevive spoke and said: "If you like, you can go on at once, and mother, Mary and myself will meet you at the great convocation a little later."

So we beckoned David to come to us. He quickly consented to be our servant again, and we planned to be off. As we were exchanging good-byes, Genevive said to David: "Go by way of the mansions of the prophets and call at the mansion of Jonah."

"Oh, Genevive," I said, "how kind and thoughtful you are for me," and after pressing my lips to hers, with a good-bye kiss, as we used to do in the world, we were soon in the chariot which was heading toward the interior of the city. Ever since stepping from the chariot at my first entrance into paradise, this had been the goal of my constant desire, to reach and see my Father's throne: for I remembered we are to reign with Him. I have already repeatedly seen our blessed Lord and looked into His holy face, but oh, I long to see His Father's throne and the hosts that must be gathering about it.

"All your desires and more," said David, "will soon be granted you, but you have been wise in not hastening to the throne, for even now you are none too well prepared for its exceeding glory. Your trip into paradise will only better prepare you for the scenes just ahead for it is better further on."

Bohemond spoke and said: "I have been very busily engaged since I saw you last, in various parts of the city, but am exceedingly thankful of this opportunity of going along with you."

"Now David, tell us about the mansions of the prophets of which Genevive spoke."

"I will be only too glad to tell you about them. Very many of the prophets and ancient men of Israel, including the patriarchs had their mansions located near together. They are so grouped that they have easy and ready access to each other. These they call their own and yet everyone has perfect privilege to go and come as he likes. It is thought no intrusion here to come and stay as long as one desires. Everything in the city belongs to each of us; we are heirs of it all."

"Oh," I said, "has God prepared all these great things for me? Are they really mine?"

"As sure as you are in the city they are yours," said David.

"I do remember the Scripture," I replied, "where God says: "All are yours and ye are Christ's and Christ is God's. (I Corinthians 3:22,23)

Bohemond spoke and said, "I am wondering about a mansion for myself and its location."

David replied and said: "Be patient, my son, God will locate you to your own satisfaction. But remember, you have unbounded privileges in the entire kingdom of heaven, both in the city and paradise. Go where you will. Come when you please, and be forever contented."

Like all the avenues and streets of the city this one was most gorgeously decorated. A branch of the river was flowing in the midst of it. On either side were growing the trees of life interspersed with many varieties of most beautiful shrubbery. No earthly camera ever made a picture even to compare to this heavenly glory.

Since leaving the children's polytechnic our chariot had been rolling along with indescribable speed. Many hundred furlongs had been passed while Bohemond and I had been talking over the experiences of each since we had parted.

"Now," said David, "we are coming near to the mansions of the ancients," and slackening his speed he said, "You can recognize the names of many of the occupants no doubt, for all who are acquainted with Jewish history will be familiar with many of the names you see yonder." Sure enough, upon the doors and posts of the verandas and other places were the names of many of the ancient saints of God.

"Now," said David, "they are always glad to welcome all the new arrivals, as well as their old friends."

I said to David: "Genevive spoke of Jonah the prophet, will we pass his mansion?"

"Oh, yes, indeed," said David, and in a few minutes the chariot halted near the threshold of a beautiful palace.

"Well, I see the prophet's name," said Bohemond.

"To be sure," said David, "and he is the veritable Jonah of the Bible. I am also trusting for you, dear brethren, that he is now in his residence."

We all sprang from the chariot and David leading the way, we were soon at the threshold. There are no door bells to ring in heaven, for everyone is always welcome. As well might a busy bee ask admission into its own hive as for one saint in heaven to have to ask another to admit him to his mansion, for there is an eternal brotherhood in heaven, with all things in common, as we know but little of on earth.

We rejoiced exceedingly when David said: "I see Jonah now through the hallway yonder."

As we entered his mansion, he came toward us and David saluted him with "Good morning, my brother."

"Good morning to you," said Jonah, "I am always glad to have you come in. Tell me who are these brethren with you?"

"Recent arrivals. Brother Sodi is a Greek of Jewish descent but later from the Scandinavian people, and Bohemond from Northern Russia."

"Glad to welcome you, dear brethren," he said, as he gave us his hand. We were soon all seated in his spacious mansion, beautiful with adornments as no earthly home has ever been decorated. As I looked about me I thought of our Lord's words on earth: "I go to prepare a place for you." (John 14:2) Oh, these many mansions, prepared by an almighty hand!" Then I thought again, "If He has made such an endless variety of flowers, sweet scented and lovely shrubbery of all kinds, with so many things to please and enhance our earthly lives, what will He not provide for His saints and His bride in heaven?"

"Well, Jonah," I said, "we are glad to meet you indeed, but tell me, are you the prophet Jonah, so conspicuous in Bible times on earth?"

"I am the Prophet Jonah, son of Amittai, reared up in Gath-helper, a town of old lower Galilee in Zebulun, more than two thousand seven hundred years ago: but that is reckoning like we used to on earth; but, dear brethren, it has really only been about two and one-half days since I came into this heavenly kingdom, reckoning by heaven's count.

"Well, do tell us, Jonah, of your experience with the whale. There has been a lot of skepticism about the story."

"The story is all true," said Jonah. "How I lived in the midst of the great fish I cannot tell. I only know I did live the three days within the fish. But he was fully as sick of the job as I was myself. I have been asked these same questions thousands of times. It is an old story to me, yet ever new and ever true because God's hand was present both to punish and to save. My continued disobedience would have meant Nineveh's destruction, but my repentance and faithfulness meant their salvation. Yes, the story is true, whatever scoffers may say — miracle indeed it was — but it was followed by the greatest revival any city ever knew. My punishment and repentance was a sign to the Ninevites. They repented — God had mercy — and I was angry, oh, sinful Jonah that I was, but He had mercy on me also, and many of the Ninevites were saved and are now in heaven."

"Oh, Jonah," I cried, "I wish you could only go back and repeat your story on earth again. Many cavilers are ridiculing the word of God over your experience."

"Yes," said Jonah, "and they will do it to their own destruction. Many great and strange things have occurred and will yet occur — some of them so strange that men will still doubt and cavil as they always have; nevertheless they are true."

"True indeed," I replied, "we have known children and animals born with two heads on opposite ends of one body, a peculiar working of some law of God producing what we called monstrosities. When other things strange occur in the physical realm, we say a miracle has occurred, and then men cavil and deny. But we are glad indeed to have met you and heard your story from your own lips. We have always believed God's word was true. Our Lord made reference to you eight hundred years after your time on earth, making you a sign of His own death and resurrection."

"Yes," said Jonah, "and it was all true, and skeptical men who were plentiful in the days of the Lord on earth, will stand at the last judgment day with the same men of Nineveh, while the Ninevites cry out against them. So will it be with latter days cavilers, who have abundantly more light than even the men in our Lord's time."

David spoke and said: "In my time many great things occurred. The hand of God was daily stretched out over me, and many deliverances He gave me — enough to fill a volume. Men in my time on earth generally accepted these special providences as God's hand in dealing with the affairs of men."

"Quite true," said Jonah, "for in my time some two hundred years after your death, everybody seemed to speak of you as one whom God greatly honored."

"Well, Jonah, we are going on to the throne, and I am very anxious to behold the glory of that most wonderful place in heaven about which we have sung and prayed all our earthly lives, and just think, I am so near to it now! Oh, hallelujah to my God! My soul is so full of raptures I cannot contain myself longer."

"Tune your harps," said David.

"Sure," I replied, and in a moment we were singing at the top of our voices: "The wonders of our God, our King."

"Oh, just think, we are in heaven, and really in the mansion of Jonah, the prophet, near to the throne."

"It has been such a pleasure to me," said Jonah, "to meet you dear brethren who have lived on earth nearly three thousand years after my time, that now we must join with you in thanksgiving to God."

So at this we all fell on our faces with adoring praises to God.

When we had arisen, Jonah said: "I hope to be at the throne during the great convocation. Millions of saints attend. I hope to meet you again at that time. So offering to us his hand, we all bade him good-bye, and were soon in David's chariot enroute for the great center of the heavenly kingdom.

I said to David: "Are we not almost as near the throne as we were when we turned back for the trip in paradise?"

"Quite as near," said David, "but we are approaching it from another quarter, at this time."

The light seemed so bright, yet not dazzling, for we were being prepared for it. Thousands of happy souls were passing us. Many loads were being made up at different points arranging for the great convocation.

"Now," said David, "we must halt, for I see an angel calling to me." He sprang out of his chariot, and, after a few minutes interview with the angel, came and said to us that he would have to leave us here for a little season, as he was called to a distant part of the city. "I think I shall leave you for only a little time. You can enjoy yourselves in such strolls as you like. Call at any of the mansions you wish. Feel perfectly at home. All you see is yours. I have to make a hasty visit to a distant part of the city on business matters concerning the great convocation. If I do not return in time for you, step on any of the chariots and you will be taken to the throne in due time." So saying we stepped from the chariot, he bade us good-bye with a lovely bow and wave of his hand, and his chariot had gone.

"Now," said Seneca, "you are weary and must rest. Sweet sleep and the peace of God be with you!" As I looked toward him, he vanished from my sight.

CHAPTER TWENTY-SEVEN

Thirteenth Visit
Conference with the Elders

Seneca came as usual and glancing over the manuscript, he suggested a few changes here and there and then proceeded as follows:

Soon after leaving David's chariot, Bohemond and I were walking alone in a deep consideration of these great marvels, and the almightiness and love of God, when we came to a lovely park into which we entered. We had not gone far until we came upon a group of the elders, among whom were Abraham and Moses, Joshua and Isaiah, Peter and John, Paul and Silas, and many others. They were engaged in a spirited conversation. They beckoned us to them, saying: "We are glad to meet you again, for we are informed that our Lord has gracious intentions concerning you."

"Well, holy brethren, we do not know what is before us, but we have found that He is full of infinite mercies and we are greatly interested in all we behold."

"We are very glad," said Abraham, "you have been wisely guided to this conference, and I have known of the extent of your visit up to this time, but we were just beginning a conversation on theology as it is now taught in the churches on earth, and if you are interested, we would invite you to remain for a time with us, and you are free to ask and answer any question you like."

We both spoke at once and accepted their kind invitation, for not often would one meet with so many men, so able as these, and the very ones who had contributed more for the faith of the church than others.

Abraham now said: "We are deeply interested in all the affairs of the church on earth, more so perhaps than those who still are in their earthly habitations and you are so recently from the earth we are glad to have you with us at this time."

"Indeed, we feel it a great privilege," I replied, "to sit with you in this conference." At this, Moses passed to us a basket of most delicious fruit of which they had been partaking. Then Abraham spoke and said: "the theology which treats of the existence, character, and attributes of God, His laws and government, the doctrines men are to believe, and the duties they are to practice, have been much neglected in recent years; and we are informed that in many branches of the church grave errors have crept in."

"Religion," said he, "is the life of man in personal communication with God. It is the recognition of God in all of our duties. It is the bond which unites man to God. That faith that comprehends His presence, and invites Him into all the affairs of man's life. It is the life of God in the soul of man manifesting itself daily in practical morality."

"What then," I asked, "is the difference between religion and theology?"

"Religion," said Abraham, "has reference to God in the heart and life of man, which sows itself in obedience to all the divine will."

"Theology," said Moses, "is a scientific system, which treats of God and the laws by which man is saved. Yet a man may be a theologian, as were many of the Scribes and Pharisees, without experimental religion. The source of all true theology is God Himself in the revelations He has given to man."

Paul then spoke and said: "These revelations are both natural and supernatural. Natural theology treats of God and His attributes as taught by nature. Nearly nineteen hundred years ago I wrote: "For the invisible things of Him from the creation of the world are clearly seen, being understood by the things that are made, even His eternal Godhead," (Romans 1:20) so they are without excuse. But the Scriptures," said he, "are the true source of correct theological teachings among men on the earth. They are a divinely inspired revelation to men. The careful interpretation of them reveals God to men as we have found Him after hundreds of years' acquaintance with Him here. They discover His true nature, attributes, relations to and dealings with man. True theology treats also of man, his relations and duties to God and his fellowmen; of the future state, which we are all now enjoying, with its rewards, and also the punishments which are meted out to the impenitent."

At this, I spoke and said: "There has been much

caviling and critical fault-finding of the Scriptures in the last few decades of time, so that I am glad of the privilege of asking you, who wrote so much of them, further concerning them, as to their authenticity, genuineness and authority as coming from God to man."

Moses was first to speak. He said: "Many cavilers and fault-finders were in my own time. No proof could satisfy them. There are mysteries of revelation as well as in the outward creation. I knew I was called and directly commissioned of God, and the books of the law were written by His express commandment. Joshua was my successor and went forth to his responsible task by appointment of our divine Lord, and his messages and writings were prefaced by such words as, "Thus saith the Lord God of Israel." Samuel, the prophet and seer of Israel, was early called of God and spake the word with authority from heaven. All the books of the prophets are composed of direct messages from God. Our Lord who sent us forth, fully recognized the whole body of our writings, included in the Old Testament Scriptures. He paid the highest honors to those ancient records, as He has fully told me. His seal being set to them they will stand forever. You need have no fears of the Scriptures ever falling beneath the feet of the church, on account of the efforts of skeptical men. God reserves to Himself the power to cause the earth to open its mouth again and swallow up the combinations of evil men, as in the days of Korah, Dathan and Abiram."

"Indeed," said Paul, "Our Lord put His full sanction to every jot and tittle of the law and the prophets; enforced the precepts written by Moses as binding upon all the Jewish people. He quoted the writings of nearly every prophet, from Moses to Malachi, recognizing their full authority, as the word of God, and giving them the distinctive title of the Scriptures, as different from all other writings. As the apostles and evangelists of our Lord, we always fully recognized their divine origin and quoted and wrote and preached from them appealing to them as authority on all questions of faith. We ever declared they were the "oracles of God, and given as the Holy Ghost spake by the mouth of His ancient servants." This is expressly declared of David, of Isaiah, and of all the holy prophets."

124

Peter now spoke and said, "You will remember in one of my epistles I spoke of our Lord's transfiguration on the holy mount and the voice that then spake from heaven attesting that this Jesus was the Son of God. Our combined testimony should have been received by every Jew. (I Peter 1:17-21) Yet, I then declared that the Scriptures were to them a more sure word of prophecy; and urged them to take heed to their revelations, for they fully spoke of Christ our Lord."

"Now," said Peter, "there are the positive assertions of inspiration and authority for all the writings of the New Testament. What the four evangelists wrote was under the eye and inspection of our Lord, although not coming to public notice for years after His ascension to heaven. A special promise of the presence and help of the Holy Spirit was given to all the apostles. The spirit of truth thus promised was to bring to our remembrance whatever the Lord had taught us, and to teach us all things. Old truths brought back to mind, and new truths brought from the fountains above, were His special delight. On account of this endowment, our Lord placed an authority on our word as upon His own and the earlier prophets'. The writers of the New Testament always identify their words as the words of the Holy Ghost, announcing their messages as in truth the word of God: the word of the Lord that should endure forever. So from God they all came. They breathe the pure spirit of His goodness and carry the stamp of His authority, and will stand forever."

"Well," said Bohemond and I at the same time, "we would be much pleased to have a brief statement or summary of their teachings as you understand them now, for we would like to compare our own ideas of theology, as also that which is now taught in the churches, with the truth as it is."

They all assented quickly, and Abraham spoke, saying, "We will hand you such a statement shortly. In the meantime, if you care, you can take a flying trip in one of the passing chariots to a praise service on Broadway, or visit the park adjoining the throne."

We thanked them for their friendly service and as we stepped on board a chariot, they said, "We will see you again soon," and waved us a pleasant good-bye. Isaiah kindly offered his services to go with us. We thanked him and the chariot soon slowed up at an entrance where thousands were gathering.

The place seemed to contain a space somewhat equal to a ten or twelve acre field in the earth. Circular seats ran the whole course round the spacious place of worship. The orchestra occupied an elevated position in the center, and a thousand harps and voices were thrilling the vast audiences with the melodies of heaven. David's harp and voice never seemed so sweet as at that service. Many fathers of the church of an early date were there, many who had suffered persecution and martyrdom were also there. Their faces glowed with a peculiar joy as their words fell like fragrant oil upon that wonderful host. At the suggestion of St. Bartholomew we all fell on our knees and faces and with one heart and voice gave God all the glory. Many short sermonettes were preached to the thousands, many of whom like ourselves were newcomers into the city. This seemed to be a preparatory service for the great coming convocation at the throne. Isaiah, with his long flowing beard, spoke as with a silver trumpet, announcing the general order newly arranged for the great occasion. Enoch's face shone equal to the angels' as he shouted the glory of his Lord. John the Baptist also with his piercing voice stirred the congregation as to a flame of fire. The blessed Virgin was also there and her sweet voice was like waves of light over all the people. We found she was held in great esteem in heaven. Priscilla and Aquilla both gave public utterances of great helpfulness. Many others witnessed to the great goodness of God. At last we all stood and sang a doxology and with one voice and as one soul shouted the praises of Him who had redeemed us to God by His own blood.

The services now closed and in passing out we saw many new arrivals from the earth, some were our own acquaintances. Oh, what joy in meeting these and to think we could now help them in their knowledge of the heavenly kingdom. They were so full of adoring wonder and praise that they could not restrain their feelings. In fact, we all felt much the same. We could not feel otherwise being in the very midst of the glory of God and in His blessed image, and in a reunion of long expectation with those of earlier years. We walked to a quiet place beneath the wide-spreading branches of a most lovely tree whose fruits were thickly hanging within easy reach and ripening every month. The fruit and leaves sent forth their fragrance delightfully and we all felt so enraptured by the presence and glory of God and the great provisions His love had planned for us; that I quickly suggested we all bow and give Him our heart-felt gratitude. We were all on our faces in a moment and it seemed our friends could never cease in saying, "hallelujah to God." I at last said: "Would you like to go back to your earth home again and leave your mansions here?"

"Oh," said one of my dear old friends as he arose and clasped my hand, "don't ask me such a question. That was only the cradle of our existence. This is our home. Oh, blessed be the Lord!"

We now gathered some fruit and communed together a long time. They told us of much of the doings of the communities we had left. I seemed to be back again, for the time being, among their homes, at their tables, driving with them along the roads and the streets, while they were speaking to me of these things. I said: "Oh, Scandinavia, my people by adoption, could I only see you all here and out of all your spiritual bondage and formality, then would I shout the praises of God greater than ever."

I then said: "If they could only know that you have brought us these tidings when they were lowering your cold body into the grave, if they could only see you here in all this glory, and us having this precious visit beneath these majestic trees of life, then they would lift their eyes on high and say, "Oh, that they had the wings of a dove, then would I fly away and be at rest." (Acts 7:56) Then with the anointed vision like the martyred Stephen of old, they might see heaven opened and the glories which the Son of God has prepared for all His children. If their eye of faith could only penetrate the veil that hides the future, if they only could with apocalyptic vision but behold these glories, if they could only hear even the echo of the melodies which we have just heard, and of which Paul caught the strain when transported to the third heaven, they would evermore say, "For me to die is gain." (Philippians 1:21) The privileges of Christ in them by the Holy Ghost would mean much more to them than they do now.

Bohemond now said: "You have unbounded liberties here. Pluck from any of the trees as oft as you like, go where you wish, enjoy everything you see. All are yours and you are Christ's and Christ is God's. We have found it wise not to hasten. You need be in no hurry. Eternity is before you."

So saying, we bade them good-bye, saying, 'We will no doubt often meet again. We have an appointment near the throne and will need to go to it; later, we hope to meet you at the great convocations at the throne itself. We will be greatly delighted to see you then."

We stepped on a chariot and were soon far out of sight or hearing of our friends. The light of the throne greatly increased, and we stepped off just to meet our elder brethren whom we left some time since.

They now handed us the roll which they had prepared, saying, "Study carefully and compare yourselves with it."

We thanked them for their great kindness and bade them a pleasant good-bye, saying, "We hope to see you again soon at the throne."

"Oh, yes, indeed," said Abraham. "We will be there, for it is of too important a character to be missed."

We now turned our faces toward a beautiful grove of shrubbery many of the trees growing in a kind of circular form with the branches drooping all about, somewhat like the weeping willow of earth. When we came near, we saw two angels in most lovely apparel, sitting in the midst, on lovely upholstery. They arose and welcomed us and laying their hands on our heads, said: "We greet you in the name of our God. But what is that in your hand?"

"A roll given us by the elders."

"Welcome to this grove and to these seats. The fragrance of these leaves will impart to you enlightening grace as you read and study." We sat down to wonder, but the angels had disappeared.

"We read and re-read the sacred roll, and rejoiced exceedingly to know that we felt in sweet harmony with the clear statements of divine truth contained in the document.

Bohemond now said: "Would to God my Bohemian brethren throughout the Austrian empire and elsewhere might only have the privilege of reading what the elders have written us."

"I was just thinking quite the same thing myself — that if the Scandinavian people as well as thousands of the churches in America and England could only study this orthodox code of divine doctrine, it might correct some of the modern errors and perversions of the faith, crept in among the people, through unfounded criticism of recent years. We must preserve this roll, for it has been prepared with great care."

We now arose and took a long stroll among beautiful flowering shrubbery and gathered such fruit as we needed. We left this quiet seclusion and joined the multitudes enroute for the throne. We had not gone far until many of the passing saints inquired concerning the roll. We read it to them aloud and discussed its various doctrinal features to the high appreciation of everyone.

Just at this time there came a chariot filled with ancient men, whom we had not met before. They were driving very leisurely along. Their chariot seemed more like the tallyho or a massive automobile of an earthly pattern. Seeing we were strangers, they at once invited us to ride with them. We accepted their invitation and the visit and the scenes which followed can never be fully described.

"You may now rest," said Seneca Sodi, "for I know you are weary and tired," and handing me the roll to be copied with care, said good night.

CHAPTER TWENTY-EIGHT

The Roll as Translated
The Elders' Creed in Brief

1.   There is but one living and true God.

His Attributes

2.   The attributes of God are the qualities, elements and perfections which belong to Him. They belong to Him and are parts of His divine nature – not that His whole being consists of a combination of the same, but because they are the forms and expressions of His being which He has revealed to man.

3.   These attributes are natural and moral. The natural attributes reveal His existence as an infinite and rational spirit; that is self-existence, freedom, omnipotence, omnipresence, omniscience, wisdom. The moral attributes are holiness, righteousness, justice, goodness, love, grace, mercy and truth.

4.   As known to men on earth God is an invisible spirit, whom no man hath seen nor can see. He is eternal and self-existent. He creates beings with immortality, but God alone possesses eternity. He is infinite, filling all space in the entire universe, embracing all worlds. He is omnipresent, i.e., infinite in power; shown by all His creations from the infinitely great to the infinitely small. All His acts are done by the exercise of His volition, and are seen by man in the universality, variety and multitude of His works. God's omnipotence is limited only by His moral perfections. God cannot lie nor do any bad act, although He has the power.

5.   God is omnipresent. The creator, upholder, and governor of all things. He is also omniscient, all things being open and naked before His eyes. God's wisdom is infinite, embracing all knowledge and is independent of all His creatures. We can tell Him nothing which He does not know, but His intelligent, infinite intuition comprehends all things past, present or future. This intelligence is perfect and absolute. Man analyzes things to find out their nature. God knows the nature without the analysis.

6.   The foreknowledge of God is also absolute. How the foreknowledge of God is to be reconciled with man's free

agency and moral accountability is indeed to men in the world a dark problem, but in the Scriptures both are clearly taught, and faith accepts what reason cannot reconcile. Some of the churches on earth have denied man's moral freedom. Others maintain that God in the exercise of His omniscience, like His omnipotence, abstains from knowing what His creatures will do under certain given circumstances. But the foreknowledge of God itself, unrevealed to men, does not impose nor even hint to me any course of conduct whatever; it in no degree affects His liberty of action. Man neither sins nor follows holiness, as the result of God's foreknowledge; so notwithstanding God's foreknowledge, He has made man in His image, a free moral being.

7. God is infinitely wise, always knows what is best, always adopts means which will best accomplish His purposes. That is wisdom; for wisdom is the art of turning to best account our knowledge. Both in creation and providence God's wisdom is seen. His wisdom and His works everywhere confirm each other as being of God. No higher wisdom has ever been seen or known than God's wisdom in the plan of human redemption. It solves the problem of God's justice in justifying the believer in Jesus Christ.

8. The perfect goodness of God is seen in the benevolence which embraces all mankind and provides for their welfare. His merciful dealings with men declare His goodness; it is also seen in His unmerited favor, drawing man to salvation and in the use of so many means to this end, also in the abundant provision which He has made for man's present and eternal happiness.

Moral Evil

9. How sin can exist in the world with all its terrible consequences in connection with God's righteous government, is an awful and difficult problem, the complete solution of which is not possible to man in his earthly life. But sin does exist, and God permits it for reasons of His own, not fully revealed to men. In heaven it could not be so. No taint of sin can ever enter the gates of this city. If an angel should again sin God would instantly cast him down to hell.

10. Righteousness and justice are divine perfections. It is holiness exhibited in government. Truth or faithfulness of God

is much the same as His righteousness. All He says and does is true. His veracity is an element of His character. God cannot lie. As God is eternal His truth remains the same. Whatever is out of harmony with His revealed truth, the same is a lie. To the question, "What is truth?" this answer which we repeat in heaven is true: "To know God as He has revealed Himself to man is truth of the highest order." Our Lord declared: "I am the way, the truth and the life." All things taught or believed that are out of harmony with His clear revelations are both false and misleading.

The Triune God

11. The eternal God has revealed Himself to men as Father, Son and Holy Ghost. The Son of God is and always was divine. He is the express image of the Father. There have been many errors and heresies in the church in past ages. But we worship one Triune God neither confounding the persons, nor dividing the substances of the same. For there is one person of the Father, another of the Son, and another of the Holy Ghost; but the Godhead of the Father, Son and Holy Ghost is one God.

The Divinity of Jesus Christ

12. He was the word of God from eternity. In the beginning was the word and the word was with God, and the word was God. While on earth we always held Him to be divine and worshipped Him as God; and in heaven He is confessed by all, both saints and angels, to be God and equal to the Father. All the hosts of heaven worship Him, He was God manifest in the flesh.

The Holy Spirit

13. The Holy Ghost is one with the Father and with the Son. Equal in eternity, power and glory. In creation He moved upon the face of the waters and developed form and beauty out of disorder and confusion. He proceeded from the Father and from the Son, and took up His abode with His church on earth. He has ever been with them since His coming on Pentecost. He

is the comforter, guide and sanctifier of His people.

Man's Original State and Fall

14. God made man upright. He was both material and spiritual and possessed of a divine life, and made in the image of God. He could hold communion with God, with all that is divine, as well as with the material universe. He was made but a little lower than the angels, and was crowned with glory and honor and had dominion over the works of God's hands in the earth. He was a companion of his Father and Creator, capable of admiring, adoring and enjoying God. While he was material and possessed an animal nature, as he came from the hands of God, yet he was an intellectual, moral, pure and holy being. He was placed under law with life and death before him. Adam rebelled; sin was born on earth. The glory of the Lord departed from him. Man fell, and felt his guilt and was alienated from God. The stream of humanity was contaminated at its source. The first pair became sinful. Their descendants of necessity were in their image fallen and depraved. So by one man sin entered into the world and death by sin; and so death passed upon all men, for that all have sinned. Our nature sinned in Adam and the stream became polluted at the fountain head. This depravity became universal for all the faculties and powers of the soul and body were brought under the power of evil.

The Atonement

15. We universally believe that the death of Christ was vicarious and propitiatory and that by it divine justice is satisfied, and God can be just and the justifier of all who believe in Christ Jesus, and that pardon and salvation is freely offered to all men, upon repentance and faith.

Election and Foreordination

16. We believe God did foreordain and devise a plan from the foundation of the world by which He would save man, and further, He did foreordain from the beginning, all men throughout the ages who would accept and be willing to conform to this plan, should be saved; so that everyone in harmony with His

power and liberty of choice who shall choose eternal life though God's plan was foreordained to eternal salvation.

Repentance

17. True repentance is a condition of soul before God wrought by the operations of the Spirit of God upon the heart and soul of man whereby he is made to see and feel the sinfulness of his sins, and also to forsake them utterly and with full purpose of heart to yield obedience to God in the future.

Justification

18. Justification can only follow true repentance and is an act of God's free grace wherein He pardoneth the sins of man, and accepteth him as righteous in His sight, only for the sake of Christ.

Faith

19. True unfeigned faith in God believes all that God has said, commanded, promised or threatened. It is dependent upon testimony, and is valuable to us as the truth itself. We can believe in men. We are responsible for our faith, for one may believe a lie as he does the truth. The truth only can make him free. True saving faith leads the soul to trust itself to the all-atoning merits of the sacrificial death and resurrection of Jesus Christ.

Adoption

20. Adoption is an act of God whereby the believing sinner is received into the family of God, with all the rights and privileges of His children in which he becomes an heir of God with a right and title to eternal life.

The New Birth

21. The new birth of which our Lord spoke is that mighty change wrought of God in the soul of man when He imparts to him eternal life and renews him in the image of God. This

change is the work of the Holy Spirit wrought in man, convincing him of sin, and leading him to repentance and faith whereby he is born from above with eternal life as a gift from God.

CHAPTER TWENTY-NINE

Fourteenth Visit
Nearing the Throne

The evening was most lovely indeed. Seneca Sodi came as usual, very full of pleasantness and joy, and glancing over the manuscript, especially the roll, suggesting a few corrections here and there, he said: "Are you ready for me, my son?"

"Indeed, I am eagerly waiting for your message," and he began:

Bohemond and I had just taken our seats in the chariot of the ancients. On inquiry we soon found we were in the chariot and the company of the earliest generations of the earth's population. We were soon introduced to Adam and Eve, the first parents of the chosen race. It seemed passingly strange for us to think we were side by side with those of such early date. Abel, Enoch and Methuselah were also in the chariot. Turning to Abel, I addressed him and said: "Oh, thou first-born son, born of those who never were born!"

"True," said Adam, who overheard the conversation, "we never were born, but created. I remember so distinctly when first I opened my eyes to behold the creations about me. I knew nothing, absolutely nothing at all. I felt the breezes and saw the waving of the branches of the trees and heard the sweet voice of birds and the lowing of cattle. God spoke intelligently to me about the fruit of the trees for food. I quickly learned how to satisfy my hunger and thirst. But I longed for a mate, for I found none among all the creations of the garden. God gave me this woman as a helpmeet for me, so I found she was "bone of my bone and flesh of my flesh," and I have loved her ever since."

At this Eve blushingly smiled and said: "You can guess our courtship was brief. It was me or none. But we soon learned life's lesson story, which all the world has repeated after us."

Seth and Noah were also side by side; Sarah and Rebecca, Keturah and Rachel also were grouped together, Ephraim and Manasseh must have seemed as young as when Jacob blessed them so long ago. Samuel and Aaron were also with the happy group and seemed to be rather presiding as prophet and priest over the chariot load. Caleb and Joshua were in the front assisting the charioteer in guiding the chariot. They all seemed to take a deep interest in us and asked us many questions bearing on modern times. After we had exchanged many questions both of modern and ancient life, I was so enraptured with the idea of eternal life, God's great gift to man, that I fairly shouted and said: "Oh, what did God mean when He breathed into man the breath of life and man became a living soul? (Genesis 2:7) Here is the explanation before me in you dear brethren, who have survived the ravages of earth and the durations of heaven and are no older than you were four thousand or five thousand years ago. Oh, blessed eternal life!"

Bohemond now spoke and said to Methuselah: "Do tell me if your years on earth were as long as it stated in God's book, nine hundred and sixty-nine years is the Bible record of your age. It seems to us almost incredible, as we only live such a short time now. Please tell us about it and what did you do?"

"Truly," replied Methuselah, "we lived to a great age and the record of the inspired word is correct, for Moses has told me repeatedly what he wrote concerning the early history of the world and man. As to why we lived so long, may be easily explained. God was exceedingly good to us. No former generations having lived before us, we had no books to read nor anything previously discovered by anyone before us. We had to find out by long searching and experimenting, which required years, which in a later day one could know in a few minutes. In fact, a child of only a few years, at a later period of the world, would know as much as one of us could know after a hundred years had passed. After all the long years of our effort we all died (except Enoch over there), and after eight hundred or nine hundred years with but little more knowledge on general lines than your children of ten or twelve years know now. In the generations of men a little later, they would live as much in seventy-five or a hundred years as we would in eight hundred or nine hundred years. So God mercifully lengthened out our lives and gave us greater opportunities toward the end for which we were placed upon the earth for our first habitation, instead of there in this celestial world. As to what we did, well, sure enough we did nothing but till the ground and herd the cattle and sheep. Our implements were indeed of the crudest sort and we made them wholly of wood. We did the best we could. Yonder sits Adam; he can tell you, dear brethren (for so you are to us), all about his early experience."

At that I arose in the chariot and was introduced again to the venerable head of the race of man, and to Eve, the mother of us all.

"Oh, Adam and Eve, tell us of your early experience in the world."

"Certainly," said Adam, "with pleasure," and Eve made a lovely bow of assent.

"Well to begin: The garden where we were first placed was a lovely home indeed. No grander place could ever be found upon the earth. I have had descriptions of all kinds of earthly gardens, but nothing equalled paradise. Everything was perfectly delightful. Fruits of all kinds were ripening and hanging ready to our hand. Nothing forbidden to us but one tree. But, oh, that sin I never can forget it! What penalties followed our disobedience! The shame, disgrace and alienation from God!

It was a sad day when God sent us out to till the ground and dig for ourselves. After we heard our sentence, we were very reluctant to leave, so there came two of the angels with scourges in their hands and without parleying they drove us out. Oh, the sorrow and tears of that day! The angels had already told us of the tree of life, and its marvelous imparting virtues. The whole garden was charged and filled with the aroma of this tree. The very breezes and atmosphere were surcharged with life, but death was creeping upon us. We felt the chill and pall of a terrible stroke. We were simply out of harmony with our environments. The curse of death was upon us, and God sent us out to till the ground which He had likewise cursed."

"Did not God show you mercy and kindness and give the promise of a Redeemer for you?"

"Surely, He did, and gave us proofs of His love toward us in the garments He gave us to cover our shame."

"Did this signify anything to you then as an offering made by blood for sin?"

"Indeed, it did," said Adam, "for God fully explained to us the conditions of pardon. This we taught to our children and Cain knew it full well as did Abel, but Cain did not believe the details concerning the sin offering and this will explain to you why Abel brought a better sacrifice than Cain and by it though dead, yet he speaketh."

"How was it, Abel?" I said.

"Just as father has told you," replied Abel.

"What about Cain?" I asked.

"He was self-willed and despised God's way. Poor boy, he sowed his seeds of unbelief and reaped his harvest among the lost."

"Will you tell me more about the results of your early sin when God drove you from the garden?"

"A thousand times I have told the story, but will cheerfully tell it again to you. Little did I comprehend before our sin the great depth and meaning of transgression. I know all that Moses wrote concerning it, and much beside, and his words were true; so also were the words of the Apostle Paul, all of which I know, for they have been repeated to me many times over. We had unbounded liberties in the garden and should have been content, but there stood the tree of knowledge very near the tree of life. God has said, "Of every tree thou mayest freely eat except one." He threatened us with death should we disobey. Why we did disobey has been the awful problem of our lives. God let the penalty fall upon us. We became mortal and subject to death. The grant of immortality was withdrawn. We were depraved, and alienated from God. We lost His image and were without hope and without God. Only through His infinite mercy were we saved, and have the privilege of these mansions of bliss."

I thanked Adam and the rest for their kindness to us and said: "We hope we can have another such interview as this with you."

"Oh, yes, we will be pleased at any time suitable to your convenience."

We now cast our eyes up the broad avenue in the direction we were going only to see it simply crowded with saints and angels bound for the Great Convocation at the throne. These were in chariots of various descriptions, or walking leisurely along, eagerly engaged in joyful conversation and pleasant visits by the way. It called to mind those great occasions in the world when ancient Israel was gathering at her great annual feast of the Lord at Jerusalem when a half million or a million souls would be gathering from cities, towns, and country throughout the Holy Land. But at this feast innumerable hosts were pouring in from all directions; those who had been gathered from all kingdoms, nations, tongues, kindreds and people of the earth, Israelites and Gentiles. No such gatherings have ever met in the world for any purpose as was gathering here.

But this time we were so near the throne that great waves of light and glory were flashing out in all directions. An earthly sunrise on a bright June morning is but a faint picture of this glory. We were yet several leagues away, but the magnificent buildings and exquisite mansions were simply beyond description.

On both sides of this great avenue were the beautiful mansions built in the early days of heaven itself, which were in those early times occupied by the first saints who crossed the threshold of time into eternity. For there was a period in eternity when no soul of man walked these golden streets, nor saw, nor enjoyed this celestial glory; but from the days of Abel they began to gather here, with an ever-increasing ratio. I was reminded again and again of our Lord's word on earth: "In my Father's house are many mansions," and truly, they had all been prepared by our blessed Lord Himself, using angels and men as His helpers.

There were also very large and spacious mansions more especially for the angels, as I was told, where they congregate and worship God and where they receive the divine commandments and from which they often start on their missions of love to yonder world of sin and sorrow.

Lovely fountains were gushing up their silvery streams of life, in the midst of the streets, and with the golden vessels of this holy sanctuary we were constantly refreshing ourselves, for the chariot was moving very slowly and leisurely along.

Enoch now said: "We are almost to the southern entrance," and with this signal we all arose in the chariot and stood to our feet. The newer arrivals were so overcome and overawed by the majesty and glory of our surroundings that we began a hymn of praise. When we had finished the hymn, we all knelt upon the seats of the chariot and poured forth our praise to God. Bohemond shouted and said: "Oh, throne of God, I am simply lost in the glory!"

Just at this moment David's chariot drove by our side. It was filled mostly with strangers, but among them was Genevive, my mother, and Mary. David had returned by the way of the

cathedral and found room for them. Now both chariots stood
still, and we all alighted, and walked but a short distance and
stood beneath the wide-spreading branches of one of the trees
of life. Here we sang another hymn and again we fell on our
faces with adoring praise. We were so overcome with the
majesty and glory all around us that we knew not what to say
or even think. Thousands of the saints were gathering about us
and pressing on nearer the throne. All those ancient men and
women of the chariot went forward at once. But Bohemond,
Genevive, mother, Mary and myself stood a few moments to
consult further with each other and with David who now came
to us. With Bohemond and myself there was a fear and an awe
we could not overcome. All the rest were perfectly at home,
and we tried to be, but felt a shrinking in our souls. The
thought of soon standing beside the throne and looking in the
face of the Great Jehovah made us think deeply of our
preparation.

David now said: "Let us go on and join the countless hosts
yonder."

Genevive and mother said: "If we are separated during this
great service, we will meet you again at the banquet following."

"Now," said Seneca Sodi, "you must rest. Faithfully trans-
cribe what I have given you and I will see you again soon."

As usual, he bade me a kindly good night, and was about to
vanish from me when I said: "Oh, Seneca, my soul is so ravished
with your narrative that I wish you would remain all night and
take me through the great congregation."

"You will hear me again, my son," he said and was gone.

CHAPTER THIRTY

Fifteenth Visit
The Splendors of the Throne

Seneca came again as usual. His face was beaming with great joy and gladness.

I said: "Why are you so exceedingly happy tonight?"

He quickly replied: "Because I am going to take you tonight where I long to be myself."

"Well," I said, "I am anxious for your message. When you left me last night, we were travelling very near the throne."

"Yes, my son, and I will tell you further of it now."

Beyond all my power of description are the splendors of the throne itself. As we approached nearer the center of the great city and to the region of the Father's throne, mighty waves of light and glory came constantly rolling over us, and with them came such refreshing baths of love, peace and joy, that our gladness was indescribable, having reached a degree of perfection never known before. The noiseless chariots were moving in all directions. Countless throngs of happy spirits, clothed in the purest garments and the expression of every face being that of the serenest peace and composure of soul were moving toward and from the throne.

Vast numbers like ourselves were approaching the throne for the first time, many of whom had been within the compass of the majestic wall a long time, but the entire satisfaction with all the surroundings and the perfect contentment of soul made them linger long at each new object with which they came in contact. It was well for them that they did, for the glory of the throne which excelleth all else would be too great for them.

I saw many who, on account of the majesty, glory and light, were so overcome, that it reminded me much of the experience of many on earth during great revival seasons, whose spiritual perceptions were greater than their nervous powers to endure, hence there followed prostrations, trances, faintings, shoutings and kindred experiences. I found even in heaven that there was a development and growth of the powers of the soul even to an endless perfection, and a strength of mental capacity unknown on earth or even at the first entrance into the heavenly state.

142

Yes, endless perfection, and still, while approaching, yet never could reach the perfection of God.

The majesty of the throne is indeed beyond description. Notwithstanding we had been graciously prepared for it, yet we were so overawed at our surroundings and the sight before us that we did not know what to say or even think. Comparisons with earthly scenes, the richest and grandest or the greatest works of man would give but a faint idea, even human language itself is too tame to tell the story. The memories of childhood experiences were constantly rushing through our minds, so that I said to myself again and again, "Is this only a dream or is it real? Have I seen a vision or am I really in heaven? No dream ever came to me on earth like this; no grandeur ever equaled it; no dream of glory so enchanting."

We had been standing spellbound a long time, when a man whose face was beaming with a halo of light, came to us; he seemed to realize our situation and said: "Dear brethren, have you just come to the throne for the first time?"

As he came near us and spoke, we thought we recognized him, but having met so many in such a short time we were not sure that he was of those in the chariot. "Indeed," I replied, "we have been for quite a little time within the city, but have been detained with so many things and wonderful scenes, that we could not reach the throne earlier."

"You have been wise," said our friend, who was interesting himself in us, "for even now you are none too well prepared for the great things which are just before you. If you would like to have me, I will accompany you for just a little while in your introduction to this most blessed and exalted place in our Father's house."

We would be much pleased to have you do so, for we are in much ignorance as to what is before us."

I turned to Bohemond and said: "How fortunate to have such company and assistance, and yet we knew that in our Father's house with its many mansions we need have no fears for our needs would be met at the right time."

"At this he brought us to a sparkling fountain not far from one of the great entrances to the throne, and with a golden goblet gave us a drink, then he went a little distance to a mammoth tree whose branches were everywhere hanging low and brought us each a cluster of its fruit, when we had eaten it, he pronounced a blessing upon us and suddenly our eyes and minds were prepared for the greatest glories to which a mortal man has ever been exalted, and to those scenes we will now turn our attention.

CHAPTER THIRTY-ONE

Fifteenth Visit – Continued
The Throne

We were so entranced at the vision before us that Bohemond fell on his face and poured forth his praise to God as I had never heard him before. In fact, we all felt completely overcome in wonder and admiration.

The vastness of the various compartments of the throne is beyond all earthly comparison. For many furlongs it was spread out in all directions before us. Bohemond came close to my side and said in a low voice: "Whoever could have thought of such glory!" Light, all filled with glory, heightened beyond all human conception of earthly things revealed the splendors of the throne beyond the powers of a man to describe, so that I kept thinking of the word which I had so long heard: "That God is light and in Him is no darkness at all." (I John 1:5) We stood long in wonder and admiration. Our guide now came to us and said: "We will now go forward and see more of the greatness of this, our Father's throne. You need have no fears, for we are all children of God and He delights in our highest enjoyment and is pleased for us to know of these treasures of His love; so come with me, and I will show you at a glance a little of what God had in mind when He laid the foundations of the earth and made man in His own image."

"I have been here during thousands of earthly years. There were but few of earth's inhabitants when first I came, compared to the unnumbered millions now; but a vast number of angels were about the throne when first I looked upon this glory."

"Yes," I said to him, "and I remember in God's word it is said: "Ten thousand times ten thousand angels are about the throne."

"Sure," said Bohemond, "and that is a hundred million and I think there is room for a hundred million more!"

We found that our guide was none other than Enoch of ancient birth, whom we had met in the chariot and also at our first entrance into paradise and again at one of the great praise services in this city. But we had met so many hundreds and even thousands in such a short time and then the bewilderment that came over us at the great sight, we were slow in distinguishing him from so many ancient men. His body shone like the light itself and he was the picture of health and youth and the man of all others, who never tasted death. "Oh, Enoch, thou blest of God!"

"Come with me," said he, and we followed him to a raised elevation many feet above the floor of the throne; from this we could see the innumerable company which John saw in his vision, or such portion of it as our eyes could reach, which no man could number. Countless throngs from all nations of earth clothed in the purest white garments. They seemed to be moving in all directions in a joyous service for their Lord.

I said in a subdued voice to Bohemond: "I wonder if John is anywhere among this mighty host, for I do remember his words how he foretold this wonderful scene: "After this I beheld and lo, a great multitude which no man could number of all nations and kindreds and peoples and tongues stood before the throne and before the Lamb, clothed with white robes and palms in their hands." (Revelation 7:9)

Enoch now said: "Shall we now go further on, for there are wonderful scenes yet before you?"

"Oh, indeed, we should like to see all."

"But," said Enoch, "you will be here a long time ere you see all."

As we passed along, we again met many whom we had seen in other parts of the city. Everyone seemed so contented and happy. They wanted nothing they did not have. There were differences in the experiences of the people, but the holy harmony was like the music of the strings of a harp; not a discord throughout the entire realm of the city or even paradise.

Enoch now led us to the throne itself. It was encircled by wonderful majestic bands of light with all the colors of the rainbow, which signified the attributes of the Almighty God and Father of us all. We seemed now to comprehend God as we never had before. I thought of the band of light that encircles the planet Saturn, the gold tinged clouds of an earthly sunset; but no comparison could describe its glory. Beneath the circle of this rainbow was the seat of the Almighty Father. For beauty, grandeur, glory and majesty, it cannot be described. It was simply upholstered glory, with all the colors of the rainbow tinging everything.

Now it will not do to think of the Almight in His greatness and power as consisting in bulk. Every attribute of the Father was in His Son, Jesus Christ. All power was His, both in heaven and earth, and while He is everywhere present at the same time, yet His omnipresence does suggest that He is a person and that person has a seat on His throne and from this throne issues the governing power of the universe. His spirit and power are operating in all worlds and His throne is likewise in all celestial kingdoms.

"Had you not been prepared for it," said Enoch, "you could not have endured this exceeding glory."

Just at this moment Moses, whom we had met at one of the fountains near the Judean gate and with whom we had such a pleasant visit, now stepped to our side, and with a pleasant bow of recognition he said: "Dear brethren, be not overawed with this glory, nor with the fear to see your Father's face, for you are in His image now. I once wished and prayed on earth to see His face; yet I knew not for what I asked. God declared to me then that no man could see His face and live, yet He veiled His face while His glory passed before me, but I did see His back parts; but now you can look upon His face and not only live, but enjoy the vision with increasing raptures throughout eternity."

"Oh, bless His name!" I said, "my soul is so filled with exceeding joy at the inexpressible glory of this scene, that I cannot restrain my feelings," so with many others who were standing quite near us and who had recently come to the throne, we fell before God with adoring praise and continued long in this attitude. Suddenly we heard a mighty chorus of voices of ten thousand times ten thousand angels, along with the innumerable company of saints, saying: "Blessing and honor and glory and power be unto Him that sitteth on the throne and unto the Lamb forever and ever."

As we arose I saw the glory of God as I never had before. His face was as the light and all His divine attributes seemed revealed and stood out in such sweet harmony that I could only think of love, goodness, mercy, power, wisdom and knowledge, and that all our needs would be supplied by Him.

I looked again, and such pure and holy thoughts filled all my soul. I thought of some lines I had learned long ago:

Eternal light, eternal light
How pure that soul must be
When brought within thy searching sight,
It shrinks not, but with calm delight,
It lives and looks on thee.

His all-seeing eyes were eyes of love. I knew that all things in heaven and earth and in all worlds both small and great, were naked and open before these eyes. His hands, I knew, had made them all.

Enoch and Moses both stood close to us and said: "We have been here for thousands of earthly years and yet we only begin to know God. You may think you have seen those eyes, yet you have only seen one ray of light to what you will see. You may think you have seen His feet, yet the earth from which you have so lately come is only one small footstool."

"Oh, yes, indeed," I replied, "I just now remember His word: 'Heaven is my throne and earth is my footstool.'"

"His greatness," said Moses, "you can never know. You see Him seated on His throne, but then His almighty spirit is everywhere. His creative skill lacks no knowledge, and His everlasting energy knows no fatigue. He is never weary in upholding all His works. His all-hearing ear listens to all rightly offered prayers. His omniscient eye sees everything. His almighty hands are quick to bless or curse. His will simply becomes almighty law."

I looked again, to scan the throne once more, and saw twenty-four seats of most exquisite beauty on both sides of the throne. I knew from the blessed word these were for the elders; but they were mostly vacant now, for the elders, I had found, are very busily engaged in service for Him who is on this throne; yes, the throne of the universe. I saw further that the throne consisted of a double compartment and I at first wondered. But Enoch came, seeing my anxious curiosity, and said to us: "Our Lord Jesus who reigns both in heaven and on earth has likewise His seat on the throne, with His Father; for He overcame and forever has His seat on this throne."

I quickly remembered the Scripture where in the Gospel it is declared, that "He was received up into glory and sat on the right hand of God"; and again the blessed martyr Stephen said: "I see the heavens open and the Son of Man standing on the right hand of God."

I said to Enoch: "Where is He now?"

"Oh, He is somewhere about the throne, or in the city; you will see Him soon, for He is always at the great convocations at this place. Have you not met Him?"

"Yes, indeed, at the Judean gate; and at a great praise service in another part of the city, but am anxious to see Him again."

"You will be delighted with inexpressible joy beyond all you have yet met or seen, when not only Himself but the great convocation of saints and angels occurs, which will be quite soon. We often meet here for further expositions of the kingdom by our Lord or His servants, and of God's further purposes with His people. We have not yet learned all there is to know about the purposes and plans of God concerning these mighty hosts of the saved."

"Those most honored of God as His servants on earth, are greatly honored here," said Enoch, "and are His ministers in heaven. These often take part in the expositions of eternal truth. Of course, you will not leave the throne until the great praise service is over?"

Bohemond came up and said: "Well, I do not think we will ever want to leave. I feel such glory in my soul. I never even dreamed while in my earthly life that such real things were in store for us."

Then I looked again into the face of Him who sitteth on the throne and said: "Oh, my God, my Father, I praise Thee forever for that Thou didst ever think of me, an unworthy mortal man, and brought me to this exceeding glory!"

"Now," said Enoch, "I must leave you for a time, for I see the mighty crowds are coming from all quarters of the city." And so saying he waved with his hand a most pleasant good-bye, as he said: "I will see you again." Moses also had disappeared among the millions of happy souls.

Bohemond and I now stood in wonder and with increasing praise to God for the great things we were now beholding when suddenly four mighty angels arose and were flying about the throne, having golden trumpets in their hands, and with one great blast they made the arches and domes of heaven ring. But they quickly disappeared through the great avenues of the city. We knew the meaning and to what followed we will now turn our attention.

149

CHAPTER THIRTY-TWO

Fifteenth Visit – Continued
Before the Throne

I turned and said to Bohemond: "What shall we do? I feel such an awe and fear, we know so little of the order of things here." We asked some standing near us in regard to it.

"Oh," said they, "have no fears, go where you like, we will all find our places, and you will be near the throne."

We widened the circle of our vision and behold we saw a vast number of seats both at the back and also at the right and left of the throne. They rose in terrace form like a great amphitheater. These, we soon found, were filling up with the great chorister of heaven. They filed in with beautiful order, each having a golden harp. At last the seats were all filled with those who had been the most devoted leaders in the choirs of earth, with very many also who never sang in an earthly concert, but because of heavenly musical voices trained in the praises of God on earth, they were chosen by the blessed Bishop of all souls in heaven for these great occasions.

I looked again. The elders had mostly taken their places, many of whom we had met. They gave a lovely bow of welcome. When all our anxieties were gone and we felt much at home.

I looked again, with adoring wonder, and lo, our blessed Lord Jesus Himself accompanied by Moses and Paul came to the throne. Our Lord took His place beside His Father; Moses and Paul beside the elders.

Countless throngs were pouring in from all directions. Chariots were bringing tens of thousands. The robes of the high priest of ancient times could not compare to the beautiful flowing draperies of these millions of the blood-washed. All seemed so happy and joyous. Many of our friends whom we had known on earth so well, and who had come from remote parts of the city or paradise now came to greet us. My own mother, Genevive and Mary were among them. Dear old grandfather, now so young and beautiful, also stood with us. Several comrades of my youth, who had passed on many years ago also came. Among them was one whom I never expected to see in heaven, but who, like the thief on the cross, was saved in last days of his life, and although he had spent a long time in the remoter regions of paradise as he afterward told me, yet now he was here. We had many congratulations and joyful unions, while the great concourse was filing in.

For thirty furlongs or more distant from our great Father's seat was the outer circle of the mighty throng gathered beneath the great arched canopy of this imperial throne. The four angels now returned and flying in the midst of the throne, were sounding through their trumpets, saying: "Holy, holy, holy is the Lord God Almighty; which was, and which is, and which is to come." When those archangels had finished this note of praise, then the twenty-four elders fell down before Him that liveth forever and ever, and sitteth on the throne, and worshipped Him, saying: "Worthy art thou our Lord and our God to receive the glory and the honor and the power for thou didst create all things and because of thy will, they are and were created."

While they were lying prostrate on their faces, the great choir of one hundred thousand voices arose and sang before the great company a new song, which for sweetness, pathos and feeling was never equaled on earth; no one discordant voice or harp was heard among them; but the music rolled up and away, and reached even with its faintest tones to those in the utmost limits of this wondrous host, for in the pure atmosphere of heaven voices can be heard for a long distance, and all the great host replied: "amen and amen." I looked again, and behold, I saw ten thousand times ten thousand angels and heard them sing with loud voices saying: "Worthy is the Lamb that was slain to receive power and riches, and wisdom and might and honor and glory and blessing." And all the elders stood and said, "amen."

They then announced a familiar hymn, familiar to earth as well as heaven, for I had heard it many years ago. The chorister led; but all the people sang and praised God until I certainly thought that the earth itself would resound with these praises and echo back the wonderful melody. I was so entranced that an awe and fear again took hold of me as I saw the greatness and wonderfulness of Almighty God as I never had before.

I looked again and an elder whom I had met, beckoned me with his hand to his side. I quickly obeyed and bounded up to the great gallery where the elders sat, and he said: "Look again at the great concourse beyond," and I saw indeed the great multitude which no man could number, out of every nation and of all tribes and peoples and tongues standing before the throne, and before the Lamb, arrayed in white robes, having palms in their hands, and they cried and shouted with one great voice, saying: "Salvation to our God which sitteth upon the throne and unto the Lamb," and all the angels fell on their faces and worshipped God and said "Amen."

After this, at the elder's suggestion, I descended to the floor of the throne and joined the company I had left, and in a low voice I said: "I never knew how to worship God before. Our love and zeal were so cold in the earth, and our worship so formal and lifeless."

"Truly," whispered Bohemond. "If I only were back to earth for one single week I would teach my people how to worship God. It does seem so passingly strange that we loved God so little while on earth."

After this little episode of conversation had passed, our Lord arose and stood and with one beck of His hand, before His august presence, profound silence reigned; and every head was bowed before Him who was our All in All.

Seneca now said: "Faithfully transcribe and I will see you again as usual. Good night."

CHAPTER THIRTY-THREE

Sixteenth Visit
The Great Convocation Concluded

I was eagerly waiting for Seneca's return, to know further, myself, the things of the throne of God. He was on time and greeted me with his usual pleasant smile and said:

As our Lord arose to speak, all heads were deeply bowed for a few moments and then most earnest attention was given. We all hung on His words as when He spoke the sermon on the mount on earth. The theme was: "The coming dispensation, now about to be ushered in, when He shall once more descend to the earth taking with Him all this mighty host of saints and angels, when will occur the resurrection of the bodies of all His saints."

The great host listened with profound attention and received the word with great gladness, for everyone was deeply interested personally in the matter. Thousands of saints shouted aloud with joy at the thought that so soon would occur the "redemption of the purchased possession."

The angels themselves were dancing for joy, for our Lord had said that they should take a most prominent part in the great event. Very many, indeed, of the unnumbered and countless host had been waiting for this even for thousands of years, and waiting for their spiritual bodies which we knew would be given us at that ime. Then we should be equal to the angels themselves, which the elders now are, and are preferred before them, for the place of the elders indicated this, being near the throne.

The pathos and feeling which our Lord manifested during this sermon was beyond anything we were accustomed to on earth. We were melted into deep emotion. He enlarged at great length on the ideas which Paul had advanced so long ago while writing under divine inspiration when he said: "having made known unto us the mystery of His will, according to His good pleasure which He hath purposed in Himself: That in the dispensation of the fullness of time, He might gather together in one all things in Christ, both which are in heaven and which are on earth even in Himself." He called attention to the superior

153

advantage the elders now have on account of their resurrection. He described to the mighty host the order of events in connection with the closing history of His spiritual reign on earth, the events of the last times, the great political changes, and devastating wars of the closing period. He declared also that in the last times great effort would be made among the leading civilized nations to bring about a peaceful settlement of national troubles. That much had been done and much remained to be done.

How quickly I thought of the words of the prophets when he wrote concerning this same theme: "They shall beat their swords into plow shares and their spears into pruning hooks." (Isaiah 2:4)

He went on to speak of the worldly character of many of the churches on earth, their loss of spiritual power, and the very great slowness of making disciples of all nations, many of the churches having almost forgotten their real mission in bringing the world back to God, as He repeated again some of His words uttered so long ago: "The church is the salt of the earth; but if the salt hath lost its savor wherewith shall it be salted?" (Matthew 5:13) As He spoke upon this point a holy fervor and deep pathos clothed His words until the mighty throng most solemnly bowed their heads with the very impressive thought that His words had a deep meaning suited to many thousands of us only a little while ago.

Oh, how many of us whispered to ourselves and to those about us, "If I only could go back even for a brief time, how differently I would live and labor for the great end for which our Lord suffered and died."

He spoke also of the fearful formalities in so many of the Protestant and Catholic churches, of the corruptions and whoredoms so extant throughout the world. As He was speaking of the degeneracy of His church on earth, I most deeply felt the force of His words uttered nearly two thousand years ago, "When the son of man shall come, will He find faith on the earth?" (Luke 18:8) "But," said He, "there is a very great throng of blood-washed souls who are looking for His return and faithfully toiling while waiting for their adoption into this mighty host above." He hinted again that the time was drawing near when He, with all this great host, with millions in paradise and all parts of the celestial city, should again go back to celebrate the earth's great sabbath.

Mighty angels with their trumpet voices should lead the hosts until the thousands of thousands of chariots should slacken their speed and slow to a halt in the regions of a terrestrial world. Then the great trump of God should be sounded, of which the blast of Sinai was but a little hint, and awaken all the dead saints who should instantly rise with spiritual bodies and each soul of us should have our own.

When He had thus spoken, all this mighty host led by the angels, shouted, "Hallelujah! the Lord omnipotent reigneth!" "And further," He said, "the living saints who have never died will never die. Death shall have no dominion over them, but from thenceforth is destroyed forever, and with them we shall be joined in one great united church, world without end." Again the great host said, "Hallelujah!"

But the most solemn and pathetic of all His utterances from the throne before the great assembly was His reference to a present condition of the church on earth. He referred to a new and most cunning device of Satan, the old enemy of man, to introduce into the church of all Christendom a most destructive criticism of the Holy Scriptures. "This," He declared, "is a revelation of the man of sin — the son of perdition, only in a new form in the last days. The mystery of iniquity was at work in the early days of the church in the various forms of the spirit of anti-Christ, but it was withheld until the Gentile world should have their opportunity of salvation. But now that wicked one is being revealed whose coming is after the working of Satan and with all deceivableness in them that perish because they received not the love of the truth that they might be saved. So they are denying much of the Holy Scriptures of God, nearly all the Old Testament saints and all that is miraculous, even assailing His own divine origin, miracles and atonement. And so God shall send them strong delusion that they should believe a lie. (II Thessalonians 2:11) "Oh, Satan," he cried, "thy doom will soon be sealed in the vortex of hell."

I can only repeat a tithe of His sermon. When He closed, a number of the elders followed Him with brief expositions of truth along some lines on which He had touched.

Many, like ourselves thought how clearly the blessed Book of God on earth has told us many of these things, and what comfort, as well as sorrow, to the saints to know the great things which are yet before us!

Far in the distance as our eyes could reach we saw the seats glittering like the purest gold, raised amphitheaterlike, to a great elevation which entirely encircled the majestic throne.

Many responsive hymns were sung, those in the distance responding with choruses, which seemed like great waves of the sea that rolled in splendor over the great throngs of the redeemed. At last, the great convocation was drawing toward its close. Our Lord now arose and with a voice distinctly heard to the utmost bounds of the throne, invited us to a royal banquet given by Himself in honor of the last arrivals. The doxology of heaven was sung by the great host. Our Lord's benediction and dismissal followed. We all repaired to a great pleasure ground adjoining the throne on the east. Many hundreds of rows of tables, more than twenty-four furlongs in length, were spread before us. These were loaded with the richest viands that paradise ever knew. A hundred varieties of the tree of life grow everywhere in the city, but especially in the valleys and upon the hillside of paradise. Twelve kinds of fruit grow on each tree. From these the tables were most gorgeously furnished. The angels were waiters at the tables and surely we lacked for nothing.

As we were eating, Bohemond arose and said: "My brother, Seneca, look at what is before us." I arose and looked across the great sea of human spirits interspersed with many thousands of angels whose delight it was to serve these honored guests. Far toward the center of this great dining hall was a stupendous fountain, a fountain of fountains. It was indeed immense in its dimensions and the height of its spray. The royal gardens, fountains and palaces of the kings of the earth could in no wise be compared to it. From this fountain we were all refreshed and also from the river of life from which its multitude of branches have their source.

While eating and drinking with the saints of all ages, and in the presence of our King, we certainly thought of the words of the book and how truly the beloved disciple had written concerning these great occasions. "And the Lamb which is in the midst of the throne shall feed them and shall lead them unto living fountains of water, and God shall wipe away all tears from their eyes. (Revelation 7:17) Indeed I thought to myself,

156

"and who can ever cry again but those of the lost ones who shall lift up their eyes, being in torment."

During the banquet the great chorister sang many new and beautiful hymns of praise. While our Lord gave everyone such a glad welcome, and especially those who had so recently entered the doorways of paradise and passed through the gates of the city and were now forever at home. Many of the ancient men and women also took part in short words of welcome.

David also tuned his harp and sang in meter the words of the beloved disciple, which nearly everybody in heaven knows. "And God shall wipe away all tears from their eyes, and there shall be no more death, neither sorrow nor crying, neither shall there be any more pain, for the former things are passed away. And He that sat upon the throne said: Behold I make all things new. And He said unto me write, for these words are true and faithful. I am Alpha and Omega, the beginning and the end. I will give unto him that is athirst, of the fountain of the water of life freely, and he that overcometh shall inherit all things and I will be his God and he shall be my son." (Revelation 21:4-7) Again the congregation shouted, "Hallelujah," and the chorister sang the dismissal.

We were now soon scattering for distant points of the city. A hundred thousand chariots were filled with the busy hosts of heaven. Salutations and momentary good-byes were heard everywhere. Smiling happy faces knew no limit to the joyful expressions and greetings with which every soul overflowed. Not one jar or discord or ruffled feeling or disappointed look was to be seen anywhere. Oh, this was heaven indeed!

When the great concourse had somewhat disappeared, there still remained an innumerable company of saints and angels. The returning chariots were bringing multitudes of others in place of those who had gone. Those who led the music and sang their sweet solos had nearly all gone. The seats of the elders were vacant, but hosts of others were crowding in. As one of the elders passed near us, Bohemond and I called him to us for a conversation.

He said, "let us step on a chariot and go to a quiet place." In a few moments we were slowing up at one of the fountains just outside one of the gateways to the throne. After giving us a drink from the fountain he said: "We will now walk to yonder cluster of trees." From them we gathered some fruit and sat

157

down to have him explain the mystery to us.

"*The revelations he gave us, I will not describe tonight. I must leave you now,*" said Seneca, "*you are tired and have need of rest,*" and he vanished from my presence.

CHAPTER THIRTY-FOUR

Last Visit
Visit with Daniel

Seneca came bright and early. His face was beaming with holy joy and light. He hastily looked over the manuscript and was pleased and said: "This part of your task is nearly done. Fully carry out all the further details and you will not be disappointed in your rewards.

When I left you last we were eating some fruit nearby a fountain on the east side of the throne and the elder, which proved to be Daniel the prophet was by our side. He now said to us: "Well, dear brethren, I am glad to have this visit with you. I know you have lately arrived in the city and are eager to know of the wonders which are constantly crowding upon you.

He told us: "Jesus our Lord, who was conceived by the eternal spirit and born of the Virgin Mary, is Lord of earth and heaven. All power has been given to Him by His Father. While I was in the earth I knew Him long before His advent by the Virgin Mary, as the "Ancient of days, whose garment was white as snow and the hair of His head like pure wool."

"In the revelations which God then gave me I saw Him 'sitting on His throne in the last judgment and His throne was like a fiery flame. A fiery stream, or bands of flaming angels, issued and came forth from before Him; a thousand thousand ministered to Him and ten thousand times ten thousand stood before Him, the judgment was set and the books were opened." (Daniel 7:9,10)

At this Bohemond clasped his hands and said: "Oh, Daniel, greatly beloved, I remember the Scripture, part of which thou hast just quoted."

"Indeed," said the elder, "and it will stand as my testimony from God till the time of the end.

He continued, "Man has been created in the likeness and image of the Triune God. In his creation he was lower than the angels, but in his redemption and glorification he is their equal and in some respects their superior. All these great hosts of the redeemed are the bride of our Lord and He is complete only in them; which is His fulness and very precious to Him. Have you

159

not noticed how completely in His image we are?"

"Indeed," I replied, "and who could have believed when we were children playing in the dirt and dusk of the earth, that all this exaltation and glory was in store for us. We were taught about heaven, but how little we conceived of its glory and grandeur."

"Sure enough," said the elder, "you have seen but little of our Father's house and the many mansions it contains. Tell me where you have been. Maybe I can help you still further in the unfoldings and knowledge of this great kingdom of God."

"Oh," said Bohemond, "we first met each other far down the river in a remote portion of paradise. We came from the earth about the same time and have been much together since we spent some time about the river and met several ancient men and learned our first lessons and hymns on the river banks."

Abraham conducted our company to the Judean gate, where we first met our Lord and received His smiles of welcome. We have visited the children's praise service at the Polytechnic and also a great praise meeting on Fourth Avenue. We also visited the Shrine of Sacred Relics, and have attended a most interesting convention of the prophets and apostles and writers of the Bible, called to discuss the condition of the church on earth, their doctrinal disputes and errors which have crept in among them from time to time, and many scenes of the deepest interest have met us at every turn since entering the city. Our souls have been constantly filled with wonder and admiration every moment of our time since leaving the earth in the angel's chariot."

"Well," said Daniel, "you have only seen the threshold of your inheritance when compared to the vastness and greatness of the provisions for you. But as to what is before you, eternity is short enough to show it all. But be assured that your enlarging cup of enjoyment will always be full. You have noticed how completely free you are from unrest and without aches or pains of any kind and that no distress or trouble burdens or haunts you here, such as we all experienced so much while in the earth, but these things are all passed away, and your appreciation of heaven is greatly increased by the bitter cups of your earthly life."

"You will have such needed employment here as will make life the most real. The government and business of your earthly life was but a preparation for and a little reflex of heaven. There is no toil here, like the sweat of our brow of which we used to know so much, but a joyful employment of all the powers of the soul to further the interest of all about us."

"Whatever you were most accustomed to do on earth will aid in your busy life in heaven. Were you in the agricultural departments of the earth, then you will often enjoy your visits to the plains, valleys, hills and mountains of paradise. These with their abounding fruitfulness and scenery will be of great delight to you and with the increasing multitudes gathering here from the earth, enlarged provisions are constantly being made for them in which you will delight to share."

"Have you been a teacher, then you will greatly relish the service of instructing those who have just come from terrestrial shores to this eternal kingdom. Those who were mechanics will find ample scope for that trait of mind in heaven. Our Lord has been preparing these mansions for us for thousands of years; but He employs the busy hands of millions of His saints in the most wonderful architecture of heaven.

"But now for you, dear brethren, all you see before you is for your enjoyment and comfort. The chariots are for your journeys. If you wish you can go at the speed of sound, go at your pleasure. Massive praise services of which we are all so fond here, are held in various sections of the city. If you wish to ascend to the higher or lower galleries or sections of the city, step into the elevator and press the number of the button and you may in a few moments be landed a thousand furlongs above or below as you desire. For you will remember that the city lieth four square, its length and breadth, its height and depth are equal, being like a solid cube, twelve thousand furlongs each side.

"Oh, how massive and great is our inheritance!" said Bohemond, "twelve thousand furlongs would be fifteen hundred miles of earthly measurement."

"Sure enough," said the elder, "and there are nearly four hundred thousand of these sections or stories of the city, beside all the vast illimitable regions of paradise. A thousand years of an earthly count will have passed before you have seen but a small portion of what is yours forever. Its vastness is beyond your ability to comprehend at present. So you see, you have ample room for the expansions of your wondering soul."

At this I clasped my hands and with great ecstatics of joy cried out: "Oh, Daniel, greatly beloved, is there no end to the provisions God has made for us?"

The elder replied: "The resources of heaven are inexhaustible, and as to the height and depth of the city, its length and breadth, you can never take it all in, but go where you will and you will find that the busy hosts of God know no fatigue and they will welcome you to any and all their banquets and feasts and services of song and praise as we have here.

"If you desire a trip to the beauties and scenery of any part of paradise, any one of the saints or angels will be glad to accompany you, for we all take pleasure in each other's comfort here. Let us now step to yon elevation at the four corners near us." We climbed the spacious stairway. "Now will you cast your eyes down this avenue toward the far distance yonder?"

We did so, and as we stood above the busy throngs and countless hosts, all who were once children of earth, and who, like ourselves, once shared in the toils and sweat of an earthly life, and with us had struggled against the fearful hosts of sin, but now exalted and glorified with our blessed Redeemer, the elder said, "Are you repaid for your faith and service for your Lord in the world?"

"Repaid," I said, "what did I ever do to merit this? No, no, it's all of grace. God is love. We were nothing; we did nothing, but cling to Jesus. He was our All in All."

"Will you now look to the north?" and he pointed with his finger the way, for we knew no north nor south, for no sun shone at noonday, nor any north star at midnight, for there is no noonday nor midnight in heaven. We needed not the light of sun, nor moon for the Lord God and the Lamb is our eternal light.

As we looked in the directions suggested, we saw the avenue was broad and lovely and the mansions were of exquisite beauty. The golden streets were as warm with so many happy people. Thousands of children were playing in the streets. Lovely fountains were throwing up their spray which sparkled like beaded diamonds of light. We saw long tables of a thousand cubits each most beautifully adorned and ladened with most precious fruits and nuts of all varieties, and with such freedom everyone seemed to be eating and drinking at his ease and pleasure.

162

I thought in what a different sense could all this mighty throng say in the same words of many of the Jews of old, "We have eaten and drunk in Thy presence and Thou hast taught in our streets." (Luke 13:26)

"Many of these children," said the elder, "have but recently come, but you see how completely contented they are. No change of place nor surroundings could make them happier, unless it would be to see their parents, brothers, sisters or friends here: then their cup of happiness would be complete indeed. They have no desire to go back to the earth from whence they have so lately come, but they do greatly rejoice in the coming of their friends. Contentment of which we only knew the first rudiments in the world is written on every soul here."

"Will you now look upward," said the elder.

We cast our eyes above. To our greater wonder still, the arches and domes above us were ablaze with the sparkle of what seemed to be the most precious diamonds for beauty, and jasper stones clear as crystal.

"This," said the elder, "is but a reflection of the glory of God which shines out from the throne and through all His works."

"Now," said the elder, "I must leave you and bid you good-bye. The blessings of the eternal God are forever yours. Great things are in store for you; but I will see you again," and he disappeared among the countless throng.

CHAPTER THIRTY-FIVE

The Last Visit — Continued

We stood a moment almost bewildered at the great scenes before us in every direction. We now descended from this great platform or elevation, to find David's chariot was standing nearby. Mother, Mary and Genevive had just stepped from it. Oh, indeed, it was a glad surprise to see them again in the midst of the great moving hosts about us. We clasped hands and with a love-kiss, clean and pure as heaven itself, we all felt that the unions begun on earth were far sweeter here than any family ever knew while in the earthly life in the flesh. But no wifehood nor husband's place is desired or hardly thought of in heaven.

David now said: "I must bid you good-bye. The visits and journeys with you have been most pleasant indeed; but I will see you all again. Gabriel with his chariot stands yonder for you. Before you go, shall we not join in one more service of thanksgiving and praise?"

Bohemond fairly shouted at this and we all took our harps and joined David in one more sweet hymn of praise. When we had finished, David waved his hand a pleasant farewell, and his chariot moved away and was lost from our gaze as we followed him with longing eyes, for we had learned to love him exceedingly.

Gabriel now came and addressed us most lovingly. Mother, Genevive and Mary all knew him well, but I had only seen him once since he bade me good-bye at my first entrance into paradise; but I found he was one of the chief angels of heaven, one of the archangels, yet he was Daniel's servant while yet in the world. I found he led the band who announced the birth of the Saviour and guarded the sepulcher at His death and rolled back the stone at His resurrection.

He now invited us to seats with him in the chariots. "For," said he, "I am sent into paradise." We accepted his invitation and were soon stepping into the first chariot of heaven, and one that has traversed the distance between heaven and earth multiplied thousands of times. In that chariot we were soon all seated.

The angel now said to mother and Genevive: "Have you any choice of routes for the journey through paradise? We have a command concerning Seneca, and you are more than welcome to journey with us to the gateway."

"Indeed," they both spoke at once, "we would be greatly pleased to go with you, and thou mayest choose the route for thou knowest best."

"Perhaps Seneca has a choice."

"Oh, Gabriel, thou blessed of God, choose thou for us, for thou hast knowledge of all places in the kingdom which we have not."

"Leaving it to me then we will go by way of the mountain regions which lie to the southeast, going out at Benjamin's gate."

"Good," said Genevive, "nothing could please Mr. Sodi better, for he always enjoyed the stupendous and romantic scenery of the earth. David, whose chariot has just gone, has very recently brought Seneca, mother and Mary with myself from the preparatory departments for children, which is far toward the southwest, to the children's amphitheater in the city where I have been for quite a time assisting the little ones in their first lessons in heaven. Seneca enjoyed the return trip through the mountain region splendidly; so I am sure thou hast chosen wisely."

"Now," said Gabriel, "when you are all ready we will be going, for we have to meet our Lord, with very many others, at the gate of Benjamin, which is toward the southeast. I wish for Seneca and Bohemond to sit with me."

We took our places beside the angel, while mother, Genevive and Mary sat together in the rear. In a moment more our chariot moved away.

"Oh, Seneca, thou blessed of God," said the angel, "thou art a chosen vessel, selected for a special errand by the Lord Himself."

"Oh, tell me, Gabriel, what is before me. Heaven has been one glad surprise at every turn since I stepped from the angel's chariot, at a distant portal of paradise when we first entered this kingdom of glory."

"Everything is before thee," said the angel, "almost nothing behind in comparison to what is yet beyond. But Seneca, thou art a favored saint of God and the unfoldings of His intentions toward thee will be made known in due time."

At this, mother, who was intensely interested in the conversation, spoke and said: "Oh, Gabriel, the man by thy side is my own son and was cared for by these hands from the day of his birth and I am deeply interested in all that is transpiring."

Genevive now stood to her feet in the chariot and leaning forward clasped her arms to my neck and said: "Oh, Gabriel, this man was my husband on earth and most sweetly were our earthly lives spent together. But here we are joined in an eternal union."

At this the angel laughed and said: "Are you married again?"

"Oh, no, we are not married, for saints do not marry in heaven, nor do they wish to; but these bonds of highest friendship will be eternal, will they not?"

"Sure," said the angel. "Your love and oneness will be far sweeter than ever it was on earth."

"But I would like to know," said Genevive, "and I know thou canst tell me, if the angels themselves were ever in love among themselves with a love similar to that of husband and wife?"

At that question, Gabriel slacked the speed of his chariot and turning his head to glance over his shoulder at Genevive, who stood with her arms still about my neck, he said: "Thou hast almost put me to blush for we are inferior to you, who have descendants and creations of your own. We have no bride neither bridegroom. But marriage was such a leading passion with the inhabitants of the earth that our Lord intends perpetuating it in eternity, only changed. He is now and ever will be the bridegroom and all the saints, you, not us, will be His bride. We were the working bees of the great family of man on earth and in heaven, neither drones nor queens, but we are all content with our sphere of action. We know no sorrow nor any unfulfilled desire which cannot be fully met here in heaven or on earth. We are your servants, and this trip to the gate of Benjamin and to paradise is my joyful service."

At this Mary stood up and said: "Oh, Gabriel, this man by thy side is my father, from whom I parted when only just an infant. I think it must have been thine own chariot which brought me to the care of dear grandmother as I learned to call her later."

At this the chariot stood still and the angel arose and turning himself about he laid his hands upon our heads with the blessings of the chief angel of God and said: "Oh, ye saints of

166

the Most High, I was present when the morning stars sang together and tuned my harp to that sacred melody of the skies. I am the same now as I was then. But before you is an endless progression, an eternal destiny, with exaltations, honors, and blessings of which you know but little now."

"Now," said Gabriel, "we must be going, for soon we must join others at Benjamin's gate."

The chariot moved on with great speed. The scenery was all new to Bohemond and myself, and Genevive said it was almost new to her. The mansions were beautiful with all the decorations that any soul in heaven could wish. Thousands of saints were coming and going, like a hive of busy bees.

"I see David's chariot," said the angel, "coming down that broad avenue yonder." In a little while we were side by side, with greetings and congratulations, for his chariot was now filled with ancient men and women; saints of renown.

On the chariots moved, side by side, we went, till at last the shining of the wall began to appear and the great gate of Benjamin loomed up before us and as we were slackening our speed, we noticed the most beautiful chariot we had yet seen standing just near the gate. It glittered with the gold of heaven, set with diamonds of beauty. Our Lord Himself was in that chariot. His twelve apostles also were with Him. Such a halo of light, almost with dazzling brightness, shown all about that chariot. In a few moments the three chariots stood side by side. We all bowed our heads, saints and angels together, before Him who had prepared this city for us.

David's harp was of great proportions. He stood before us all and announced a hymn. We all arose and sang again; while standing in the chariot, the praises of our Lord and Redeemer.

The angel, Gabriel, sang with loud hosannas an ancient solo. Daniel, who was in David's chariot, and who was a fast friend of the angel, said: "Sing it again," and surely the sweetest music to which we had ever listened rolled from his hallowed lips.

"Now," said the angel, "look through this gateway," and behold, there was an immense company of new arrivals standing just outside, and singing some new songs. This company had been escorted here from different places in paradise much the same as we had been only a short time ago. Stephen, the martyred saint, had led this company. While he was getting them ready to pass through the gateway into the presence of their

Lord Jesus, who now beckons us all to a raised elevation close beside the gateway, He laid His hand gently on my head and said: "Son, be of good cheer, thy earthly mission is not yet completed, but as I once called Moses and Elias from these shining gates, so now I send thee to make known what thou hast seen and heard, which is but a tithe of what thou shalt yet see, but this is all they will receive at thy hand now. True unfeigned faith in many sections of the earth is waning. Thou wilt find a faithful helper, on whose head my blessings shall rest. When thou has completed thy journey to the earth, I shall confer the elder's blessing upon thee — an earlier inheritance of the "purchased possession." All heads were now bowed, while He prayed and committed me to the angel's care.

Bohemond and the women came close to my side and said: "Is it true we must part?"

"Only for a time, yes, only for a time." And with an exaltation, I cried: "I shall soon see you again."

The Lord said: "Hasten to thy mission, I must welcome these outside the gate, for I have redeemed them by my blood." So saying, He called Gabriel to His side and gave him a charge concerning me. I bade my kindred and all those who came to see me off good-bye, saying: "I will see you again," and I mounted the angel's chariot.

CHAPTER THIRTY-SIX

Seneca's Return to the Earth

The angel now was seated by my side and his chariot moved slowly away. As I looked backward while we were passing through the great arch of the gateway, I saw many of them waving with their hands a good-bye blessing.

We were soon passing beside the great company who were eager to enter the gateway. We gave them all a bow of recognition, saying, "We will see you all again." We were soon beyond the hearing of their voices. As the chariot vanished from their view, we were rapidly flying along an immense roadway, leading them from the gate of Benjamin to distant places of paradise. Great fruitful valleys spread out everywhere, and thousands of busy saints were gathering the ripening fruits.

"Now," said Gabriel, "yonder are the mountaineous regions of paradise of which I spoke; shall we go past them?"

"Oh, angel, my cup of blessing seems full and will contain no more. The burden with which I am charged, is absorbing all my thoughts, but if thou art willing, just a hasty flight by the foothills will please me much and suffice my curisoty."

He quickly turned his chariot to a side road leading up the mountain slopes. Rapidly we were mounting those stupendous heights. On a lovely plateau half way up the mountain summit, Gabriel brought his chariot to halt just to allow me to look abroad over the vast plains and valleys of paradise. Immense gardens of beauty, filled with all varieties of fruits and blooming shrubbery were spread out as far as the eye could reach. I could see at a glance multiplied thousands of busy saints and angels enjoying these luxuries of heaven. My soul was so filled with the ecstatics of glory and praise for these exalted privileges which our good Father had granted me, and the honors conferred upon a mortal man of earth, that I was simply lost in wonder and fell down at the feet of the angel with adoring praise to God. "Oh, Gabriel, stay thy hand of blessing, my cup runneth over."

"Now, Seneca, we must resume our journey." With great speed the chariot darted down the great hillsides and across the valleys, through lovely parks and pleasure grounds of paradise. Thousands of honored saints have their mansions in the various sections of this romantic scenery of heaven. I was so overcome with the grandeur of this section of paradise, that I fell down at the feet of the angel again and poured forth my praise to God with loud hosannahs. I arose and the angel pointed toward a great paradisical arch in the far distance. Toward it he was steering his chariot. The trees of life were growing everywhere. The aroma of the leaves made the breath of heaven fragrant with their life-imparting virtue. No picture on earth could ever suggest such glory as this.

The angel drove his chariot slowly amidst deep gorges and past sparkling fountains and where groups of men and women were going and coming, or refreshing themselves at the fountains and with the fruit of the trees of life. I said to the angel again: "What a place to spend the leisure hours of eternity, in rest and recreation! Surely this is heaven!"

The angel now turned to me and asked if I recognized him. "Oh, Gabriel, at the throne I saw thee."

He said: "Think again. When thou didst leave thy earthly habitation for this most favored tour of heaven."

"Oh, angel, thou broughtest me to the gates of the kingdom."

"Indeed," said the angel, "and I have a further mission for thee. Only a glimpse of the heavenly inheritance and the greatness of our Father's house hast thou yet seen, but eternity is yet before thee and it alone will suffice to satisfy thy wondering soul. But now a little quiet rest is needed before thy further mission begins and ere we pass through that great archway yonder."

Gabriel drove his chariot very slowly along. Hundreds of new arrivals were to be seen with their first rapture of delight in heaven. This I knew from their conduct, so much like my own had been. Some just stepping from the chariots were shouting as we had done.

On, the chariot went, toward the great archway of paradise. I leaned my head on the shoulder of the angel and for the first time felt a kind of drowsiness come over me. I slept: how long, I do not know, but when I awoke, the chariot was standing still at the threshold of the old home at the foothills of the Cascades.

I stepped out and was met by two angels who led me within. I said: "Is it true that I am back again to my earthly home?" Sure enough, for there lay my body which had been carefully guarded by my faithful servants, Sena and Serva, who had previous instructions for no burial for fifty days. More than forty had already passed and yet upon the body though cold and in the slumbers of death, no signs of decay were seen. It was midnight and the watchers were sound asleep. Gabriel now joined us and laying his hand upon the faces of those who slept, there followed the deep sleep which came over Adam while Eve was being formed from his rib. So no one of the sleepers knew of our presence. Gabriel now passed his hand over the lifeless body and instantly it sprang into life with a mighty change from mortality to immortality. In a moment it was my own again. I shouted: "Oh, glorious body! Oh, redemption of the purchased possession! Mighty change — from death to immortality!" Oh, how quickly I thought of the words of Paul: "For our conversation is in heaven, from whence also we look for the Saviour, the Lord Jesus Christ, who shall change our vile body, that it may be fashioned like unto His glorious body." I stood a moment in wonder, not knowing what to say. I was so overcome with the glory of God, but body and soul became as one.

I now said to the angel: "Who will assist in this work committed to me?"

He quickly directed me to you, my son, explaining the place of your home; "but we will not leave thee," they said, "until all things are adjusted. Now leave thy earthly home and all therein. They will take care of themselves. Come to the chariot."

The Cascades and the Rockies were passed and the valley of the Mississippi was soon behind us. Near your humble village the chariot alighted. I have crossed the continent to find you, my brother, and now I am so glad you have so willingly and cheerfully assisted in this work. I have examined your manuscript and approve of what you have done. Let the printer take it from your hands. Put it before the people. Some will not approve, others will bless God. But if you faithfully complete your task, the blessing of Almighty God will be upon you.

He then came and pressed a kiss upon my forehead and turning away, he said: "Farewell, my son. The blessings of the eternal God be thine, blessing thee both in basket and in store. The eternal God shall be thy refuge and underneath shall be the everlasting arms. (Deuteronomy 33:27) He shall convert thine enemy to thy friend, and the angels which so faithfully guarded my mortal body, shall be guard about thy soul." Again he pressed my hand in his, kissing it again and again, and lifting up his eyes and hands toward heaven, he pronounced the blessing of heaven upon me, and in closing said: "The angel is waiting for me," and he vanished out of my sight. I quickly followed to the door, but he was gone, for the chariot had borne him aloft.

GWEN SHAW'S AUTOBIOGRAPHY!

UNCONDITIONAL SURRENDER—*Gwen Shaw*. The life story of Gwen R. Shaw, lovingly known as "Sister Gwen" to thousands of people in over one hundred nations. You will laugh and cry with her as you feel the heartbeat of a great woman of God who has given all to Him, asking only for souls in return. Your life will be challenged as you walk with her through mission field after mission field. You will never be the same when you read how God pours out His Spirit and confirms His Word.Hardcover #106-82 $19.95
....video NTSC (North American format) #GSL-99 $20.00
....video PAL (European format) #GSLP-99 $20.00

DAILY DEVOTIONALS BY GWEN SHAW

DAILY PREPARATIONS FOR PERFECTION —*Gwen Shaw*. This daily devotional comes to you exactly as the Holy Spirit spoke to the author's heart in her own private devotions. You will feel that Jesus is speaking to you every time you open it. It is loved by all; read and re-read
....Paperback #101-32 $12.50
DAY BY DAY—*Gwen Shaw*. The author's daily devotional book based on the Psalms will give you an inspiring word directly from the Throne Room each day to fill your heart with praise to God. It was a great comfort to the author herself after the fire in 1990 that destroyed so much. (Also available in French) ....Hardcover #101-38 $18.50
FROM THE HEART OF JESUS—*Gwen Shaw*. This devotional book is like no other. It will take you back to Bible days and you will walk and talk with Jesus and His disciples as he ministered to the people, as He suffered and died and as He rose again from the dead. These words from the heart of Jesus will go straight to your heart, bringing comfort, peace encouragement and hope! 923 pages ....Hardcover #102-11 $29.95
GEMS OF WISDOM — A daily devotional based on the book of Proverbs — *Gwen Shaw*. In the Proverbs you will find instruction for upright living, honesty, justice and wisdom. Every word in the Proverbs applies to today's problems as when they were first written. If you are going through great difficulties and facing problems which seem to have no solution, you will find the answer in these Proverbs. You'll have a Proverb and an inspired writing about it for each day of the year ....Hardcover #105-49 $25.95
IN THE BEGINNING — A daily devotional based on the book of Genesis — *Gwen Shaw*. The Book of Genesis is perhaps the most important Book in the Old Testament. It is the foundation stone of all knowledge and wisdom. Deep and wonderful truths hidden in the pages of Genesis are revealed in this devotional book. You'll be amazed at the soul-stirring writings inspired by the well-known stories of Genesis ....#115-47 $27.95

CLASSIC ANOINTED BIBLE STUDIES

BEHOLD THE BRIDEGROOM COMETH!— *Gwen Shaw*. A Bible study on the soon return of Jesus Christ. With so many false teachings these days, it is important that we realize how imminent the rapture of the saints of God really is ....#100-37 $6.50

ENDUED WITH LIGHT TO REIGN FOREVER — *Gwen Shaw*. This deeply profound Bible study reveals the characteristics of the eternal, super-natural, creative light of God as found in His Word. The "Father of Lights," created man in His image. He longs for man to step out of darkness and into His light ....#101-71 $6.00

GOD'S END-TIME BATTLE-PLAN—*Gwen Shaw*. This study on spiritu-al warfare gives you the biblical weapons for spiritual warfare such as victory through dancing, shouting, praising, uplifted hands, marching, etc. It has been a great help to many who have been bound by tradition ....#102-35 $8.00

IT'S TIME FOR REVIVAL—*Gwen Shaw*. A Bible Study on Revival that not only gives scriptural promises of the end-time Revival, but also presents the stories of revivals in the past and the revivalists whom God used. It will stir your heart and encourage you to believe for great revival ......#103-24 $7.75

OUR MINISTERING ANGELS—*Gwen Shaw*. A scriptural Bible study on the topic of angels. Angels will be playing a more and more promi-nent part in these last days. We need to understand about them and their ministry ....#104-87 $7.50

POUR OUT YOUR HEART—*Gwen Shaw*. A wonderful Bible study on tra-vailing prayer. The hour has come to intercede before the throne of God. The call to intercession is for everyone, and we must carry the Lord's burden and weep for the lost so that the harvest can be brought in quickly ....#105-16 $5.00

REDEEMING THE LAND—*Gwen Shaw*. This important teaching will help you know your authority through the Blood of Jesus to dislodge evil spir-its, break the curse, and restore God's blessing upon the land. A Bible study on spiritual warfare...#108-61 $9.50

THE FINE LINE—*Gwen Shaw*. This Bible study clearly magnifies the "fine line" difference between the soul realm and the spirit realm. Both are intangible and therefore cannot be discerned with the five senses, but must be discerned by the Holy Spirit and the Word of God. A must for the deep-er Christian...#101-91 $6.00

THE POWER OF THE PRECIOUS BLOOD—*Gwen Shaw*. A Bible study on the Blood of Jesus. The author shares how it was revealed to her how much Satan fears Jesus' Blood. This Bible study will help you over-come and destroy the works of Satan in your life and the lives of loved ones ....#105-18 $5.00

THE POWER OF PRAISE—*Gwen Shaw*. When God created the heavens and earth He was surrounded by praise. Miracles happen when holy people praise a Holy God! Praise is the language of creation. If prayer can move the hand of God, how much more praise can move Him! ....#400-66 $5.00

YE SHALL RECEIVE POWER FROM ON HIGH *Gwen Shaw.* This is a much needed foundational teaching on the Baptism of the Holy Spirit. It will enable you to teach this subject, as well as to understand these truths more fully yourself ....#107-37 $5.00

YOUR APPOINTMENT WITH GOD—*Gwen Shaw.* A Bible study on fasting. Fasting is one of the most neglected sources of power over bondages of Satan that God has given the Church. The author's experiences are shared in this Bible study in a way that will change your life ....#107-40 $5.00

IN-DEPTH BIBLE STUDIES

FORGIVE AND RECEIVE—An In-Depth Bible Study on Philemon for the Serious Student of God's Word—*Gwen Shaw.* This Bible Study is a lesson to the church on the much-needed truths of forgiveness and restoration. The epistle to Philemon came from the heart of Paul who had experienced great forgiveness ....#102-01 $7.00

GRACE ALONE—An In-Depth Bible Study on Galatians for the Serious Student of God's Word—*Gwen Shaw.* This study teaches the reader to gain freedom in the finished work of the Cross by forsaking works which cannot add to salvation and live by *Grace Alone* ....#108-47 $13.00

MYSTERY REVEALED—An In-Depth Bible Study on Ephesians for the Serious Student of God's Word—*Gwen Shaw.* Search the depths of God's riches in one of Paul's most profound epistles, "to the praise of His glory!" Learn the "mystery" of the united Body of Christ........#104-53 $15.00

OUR GLORIOUS HEAD—An In-Depth Bible Study on Colossians for the Serious Student of God's Word—*Gwen Shaw.* This book teaches vital truths for today, assisting the reader in discerning false teachings, when the philosophies of men are being promoted as being the truths of God. Jesus Christ is the Head of His Body ....#104-85 $9.00

THE CATCHING AWAY!—An In-Depth Bible Study on First and Second Thessalonians —*Gwen Shaw.* This is a very timely Bible Study because Jesus is coming soon! The book of I Thessalonians explains God's revelation to Paul on the rapture of the saints. II Thessalonians reveals what will happen after the rapture when the antichrist takes over ....#100-88 $13.00

THE LOVE LETTER—An In-Depth Bible Study on Philippians for the Serious Student of God's Word—*Gwen Shaw.* Another of Gwen Shaw's expository Bibles Studies on the books of the Bible. This study of the letter to the first church of Europe will give the reader an understanding of Paul's great love for the church that was born out of his suffering ....#103-99 $9.00

BIBLE COURSE

THE TRIBES OF ISRAEL—*Gwen Shaw.* This popular and well-loved study on the thirteen tribes of Israel will show you your place in the spiritual tribes in these last days. Better understand yourself and others through the study of this Bible Course ....#106-70 $45.00

HASTENING OUR REDEMPTION — *Gwen Shaw*. All of Heaven and Earth are waiting for the Body of Christ to rise up in maturity and reclaim what we lost in the Fall of Man. Applying the Blood of Jesus is the key to *Hastening Our Redemption* ....#116-53 $1.50

IT CAN BE AVERTED — *Gwen Shaw*. Many people today are burdened and fearful over prophecies of doom and destruction. However, the Bible is clear that God prefers mercy over judgment when His people humble themselves and pray ....#116-85 $1.50

KAIROS TIME — *Gwen Shaw*. That once in a lifetime opportunity—that second, or minute, or hour, or year, or even longer, when a golden opportunity is sovereignly given to us by the Almighty. What we do with it can change our lives and possibly even change the world ....#200-06 $1.50

KNOWING ONE ANOTHER IN THE SPIRIT—*Gwen Shaw*. Experience great peace as you learn to understand the difficulties your friends, enemies and loved ones face that help to form their character. *"Wherefore henceforth know we no man after the flesh.."* (II Corinthians 5:16a). An anointed message in booklet form ....#103-62 $1.50

THE CRUCIFIED LIFE—*Gwen Shaw*. When you suffer and you know the cause is not your own sin, for you have searched your heart before God; then you must accept that it is God doing a new thing in yoru life. Let joy rise up within you because you are a partaker of Christ's suffering ....#115-61 $1.50

THE MASTER IS COME AND CALLETH FOR THEE — *Gwen Shaw*. Read about how the Lord called Gwen Shaw to begin the ministry of the End-Time Handmaidens and Servants. Perhaps the Master is also calling you into His service. Bring Him the fragments of your life — He will put them together again. An anointed message booklet ....#104-31 $1.50

WOMEN OF THE BIBLE SERIES

EVE—MOTHER OF US ALL — *Gwen Shaw*. Discover the secrets of one of the most neglected and misunderstood stories in history ....#117-50 $4.50

MIRIAM—THE PROPHETESS — *Gwen Shaw*. The first female to lead worship, the first woman given the title "Leader" of God's people by the Lord ....#M400-67 $7.50

SARAH—PRINCESS OF ALL MANKIND — *Gwen Shaw*. Feel the heartbeat and struggles of this woman who left so great an impact for all time ....#117-51 $4.50

REBEKAH—THE BRIDE — *Gwen Shaw*. The destiny of the world was determined when she says three simple words, "I will go!" ......#117-52 $4.50

LEAH AND RACHEL—THE TWIN WIVES OF JACOB — *Gwen Shaw*. You will feel their dreams, their pains, their jealousies ....#200-46 $4.50

BOOKS PUBLISHED BY ENGELTAL PRESS

ATTITUDES IN THE BEATITUDES — *Esther Rollins.* Esther taught this anointed course on the Beatitudes as a guest teacher at our School of Ministry and an instructor of the Word of God for 50 years. Both basic and profound, this dynamic teaching is full of insight for the Christian walk ....#115-72 $5.95

BANISHED FOR FAITH — *Emil Waltner.* The stirring story of the courageous forefathers of Gwen Shaw, the Hutterite Mennonites, who were banished from their homeland and suffered great persecution for their faith. Republished with an index and epilogue by Gwen Shaw ....#100-33 $12.95

BECOMING A SERVANT — *Robert Baldwin.* Learn what is on God's heart about servanthood. We must learn to serve before we can be trusted to lead. If you want to be great in God's Kingdom, learn to be the servant of all ....#118-55 $2.00

FOOTPRINTS — *Larry Hunt.* A collection of poems and stories reflecting the hand of God upon this humble pastor during 35 years of ministry ....#114-25 $3.75

FROM DUST TO GLORY — *June Lewis.* The Lord intends more than just salvation for us. He is making vessels of eternal Glory if we submit to Him. A collection of poems and stories reflecting the hand of God upon this humble pastor during 35 years of ministry ....#102-07 $7.50

HOLY ANN — *Helen Bingham.* This humble Irish woman moved the arm of God through simple faith and prevailing prayer. Read these modern miracles that are told like a story from the Old Testament. The record of a lifetime of answered prayer ....#110-38 $4.95

IT WAS WORTH IT ALL — *Elly Matz.* The story of a beautiful woman whose courage will inspire you. Feel HER heart as she tells of her starving father, the young Communist engineer she married, the villages mysteriously evacuated, the invading German army, the concentration camp where she was a prisoner, and her escape into freedom ....#115-70 $5.95

LET'S KEEP MOVING — *Pete Snyder.* Travel with Peter to Haiti where he struggles with the call of God to be a missionary. Identify with Peter's growth of faith through trials and tribulations as he travels on to China where new adventures await and a kind endurance is needed ....#115-71 $9.95

RULING IN THEIR MIDST — *June Lewis.* The Lord has called us to rule even in the midst of all demonic activity and Satan's plans and schemes. Sister June has learned spiritual warfare from the Lord Himself, "who teacheth my hands to war," in the face of personal tragedy...#108-73 $6.00

THE EYE OF THE NEEDLE — *Charlotte Baker.* These heavily anointed, life-changing prophetic parables will be used of the Holy Spirit to touch the depths of you and minister to your greatest needs ....#113-22 $3.00

THE GOLDEN AGE OF RETIREMENT — *Gen Siewiorek*. With humor and spiritual insight the author welcomes you to the world of retirement homes. She examines such sensitive and painful issues as losing one's independence, adjusting to the food and activities of retirement home living and facing what it means to grow old and eventually die ......#G400-68 $10.95

THE STORY OF THE GLORY — *Robert Doorn*. The Glory of God has followed Drs. Robert and Glenyce Doorn throughout their fifty years of ministry. You will be blessed as you witness almost every great move of God through their eye...#118-77 $9.95

WESLEY'S SERMONS — *John Wesley*. Five sermons by this great saint whose love and compassion for souls helped produce the Great Awakening ....#107-00 $4.50

BOOKS RECOMMENDED BY ENGELTAL PRESS

AWAKENED BY AN ANGEL — *Carl W. Hahn, Jr*. Read the daily and nightly accounts of a retired denominational pastor who has been seeing light forms of angels and recording his experiences ever since ....#A400-26 $12.00

EDITED BY AN ANGEL — *Carl W. Hahn, Jr*. The continuing saga of Rev. Hahn's experiences as his Guardian Angel Precious assists in editing his book from his daily and nightly visitations ....#E400-030 $12.00

EVIDENCES OF THE FOOTPRINTS OF GOD— *Tommy Schmidt*. You will be thrilled with some of the wonderful facts and truths of the science of creation and the mysteries of the creative works of God ....#E118-69 $15.00

OH THAT ISHMAEL MIGHT LIVE — *Gene Little*. Through the author's love for the Muslim people which grew out of his journeys to the nations of this world, learn to overcome your fears and ignorance and bring life to Abraham's forgotten sons and daughters ....#O116-56 $15.00

TO LOVE A STRANGER — *Gene Little*. A biblical study introducing you to the blessings of hospitality and honors given to a Christian through the ministry of an open heart and open door ....#T113-11 $5.00

WELLSPRING OF WISDOM — *Gene Little*. The stories Jesus told centuries ago are as fresh today as they were two thousand years ago. Each generation has tried to catch these truths and insights. Be renewed in your faith and refreshed in the Spirit of Jesus through His parables ....#W300-38 $15.00

BOOKS ABOUT HEAVEN

INTRA MUROS — *Rebecca Springer*. One of the most beautiful books about Heaven available in its unabridged form. Read the glorious account of this ordinary believer's visit to Heaven ....#103-19 $8.00

PARADISE, THE HOLY CITY AND TH GLORY OF THE THRONE — *Elwood Scott*. Visited by a saint of God who spent forty days in Heaven, Elwood Scott's detailed description will edify and comfort your heart. Especially good for those with lost loved ones ....#104-97 $8.00

CHILDREN'S BOOKS

LITTLE ONES TO HIM BELONG—*Gwen Shaw*. Based on the testimonies of children's visions of Heaven and the death of a small Chinese boy, Sister Gwen weaves a delightful story of the precious joys of Heaven for children of all ages ....#103-88 $9.00

TELL ME THE STORIES OF JESUS—*Gwen Shaw*. Sister Gwen takes some of the greatest New Testament Stories of the Life of Jesus and writes them in a way that will interest children and help them to love Jesus........#106-37 $9.00

PROPHECIES AND VISIONS

THE DAY OF THE LORD IS NEAR: Vol. I - IV—*Engeltal Press*. "Surely the Lord GOD will do nothing, but he revealeth his secret unto his servants the prophets." (Amos 3: 7) A collection of prophecies, visions and dreams. This startling compilation will help you understand what God has in His heart for the near future ....$10.00 each ....Volumes I - IVwith binder #119-99 $25.00

Prices are subject to change without notice.
You may obtain a current price list from

Engeltal Press
P.O. Box 447 • Jasper, Ark. 72641
Phone (870) 446-2665 • Fax (870) 446-2259
www.engeltalpress.com